Connect to NCTM Standards 2000

Making the Standards Work at Grade 1

Francis (Skip) Fennell, Ph.D.
Honi J. Bamberger, Ph.D.
Thomas E. Rowan, Ph.D.
Kay B. Sammons
Anna R. Suarez

Acknowledgments

Project Editors → Diane Nieker, Jeff Stiegel

Writers → Tim Burnett, Marilyn Davis, Beth Sycamore

Writing and Editorial Services → MathLink, Inc.

Design Director → Karen Stack

Design → Gerta Sorensen-London

Project Coordinator → Barbara Quincer

Cover Illustration → Jim Dandy

Illustrators → Susan Aiello, Jim Dandy, Sarah Frederking

Production → Inkwell Publishing Solutions, Inc

Manufacturing → Dallas Richards

Two Prudential Plaza

Chicago, IL 60601

ISBN 0-7622-1243-8

Catalog No. 21108

Customer Service 800-624-0822

http://www.creativepublications.com

1 2 3 4 5 6 7 8 MAL 05 04 03 02 01 00

Contents

Overview

Since *Curriculum and Evaluation Standards for School Mathematics* was released in 1989, much has been learned about how ideas work in the classroom and how children learn mathematics. The release of the *Principles and Standards for School Mathematics* creates an opportunity for us to examine our goals, our math curricula, and our teaching methods in light of these new insights and to consider practices and procedures that will improve school mathematics education. As did the original draft, *Principles and Standards* promotes ways for all educators to strengthen the teaching and learning of mathematics by addressing two important concerns: the characteristics of instructional programs that will provide high-quality mathematical experiences for children as they progress through school, and the mathematical content and processes children should know and use as they advance from grade to grade.

Content Standards

Number and Operation

Algebra

Geometry

Measurement

Data Analysis and Probability

Process Standards

Problem Solving

Reasoning and Proof

Communication

Connections

Representation

General Overview

Connect to NCTM Standards 2000 is designed to help you understand and implement the NCTM standards. Regardless of your teaching style, the information presented in this book will help you to make the standards work. *Principles and Standards* identifies ten standards. Five of those standards are described as content standards that organize all of mathematics into five broad areas of learning; they address *what* children learn. The other five standards, the process standards, are concerned with *how* children learn and how information is presented.

Today, more than ever, there is a need for all children to have a strong base in mathematics. This means that children do not just memorize facts and procedures, but that they have an understanding of mathematics and mathematical thinking. The interplay between content and process is complicated, but integrating the two is critical if our children are to receive the mathematics education they will need to function effectively in the world they will grow into.

The lessons contained within *Connect to NCTM Standards 2000* are organized into sections by content. Each section contains four lessons dealing with some aspect of that content standard. Each lesson demonstrates ways to develop the content by using the process standards. An overview highlights grade-level content skills and gives a brief description of the four lessons for that standard.

The last section of the book, entitled Create Your Own Lesson, is designed to help you develop lessons of your own that will comfortably incorporate the NCTM standards with your teaching style.

About the Lessons

Each content standard section contains four lessons that address some aspect of the content at the grade level. Three of the lessons have been specially developed to model ways the process standards can be used to develop the content being presented. The fourth lesson examines a hypothetical math textbook lesson in terms of how the process standards are incorporated into that lesson. Suggestions are offered for increasing the focus on three of the five process standards to create a more effective lesson. Then, a lesson is presented modeling how those suggestions can be implemented.

As you read through the lessons, keep in mind that what is offered is only one possible approach. You might have a completely different idea about how to develop the concept, and that's fine. These lessons are intended to provide examples of how the process standards can work to make mathematics lessons more meaningful, and to model questions and techniques that you might incorporate into your teaching. As you read through the lessons, pay attention to how the process standards are being used. Use the ideas presented as a springboard for your own ideas.

Each lesson is intended for a single class period. Some introduce a concept, others require that children have some experience with the concept, and still others are meant to be used at the end of a unit. As you examine these lessons, think about how and where they fit into your curriculum. Any of the lessons here can be used as a replacement for the comparable lesson in your current math program. Try the lessons and see the difference incorporating the process standards can make.

Creating Your Own Lessons

The last section of the book is designed to help you develop lessons of your own that incorporate the NCTM standards and are compatible with your teaching style. You will find questions to help you focus on ideas to consider as you begin to organize a standards-based lesson. You will also have an opportunity to follow the thoughts and decisions one person used in the process of developing a lesson.

About the Authors

Francis (Skip) Fennell, Ph.D.

Dr. Fennell was a member of the writing team of *Principles and Standards for School Mathematics* (NCTM, 2000). He has authored mathematics textbooks, materials for both children and teachers, and numerous articles for leading mathematics journals. Dr. Fennell has served on the Board of Directors of NCTM and as Program Officer of instructional materials and teacher enhancement within the Division of Elementary, Secondary, and Informal Education at the National Science Foundation. He has been selected as Outstanding Mathematics Educator by the Maryland Council of Teachers of Mathematics, and as Professor of the Year by both the Carnegie Foundation and Western Maryland College, where he is a professor of education.

Honi J. Bamberger, Ph.D.

Dr. Bamberger is a recognized math scholar and teacher. She has taught at both the elementary school and college levels, served as an associate research scientist and mathematics consultant for Johns Hopkins University, and contributed as a consultant and content writer for the "Numbers Alive" public television series. Dr. Bamberger has presented her research findings at mathematics conferences across the country, and has been an author for a number of mathematics textbooks. Currently, Dr. Bamberger is executive director of Insight, a consulting firm specializing in professional development in mathematics education.

Thomas E. Rowan, Ph.D.

Dr. Rowan was a member of the working group that wrote the K–4 section of the *Curriculum and Evaluation Standards for School Mathematics.* Since the Standards were first published, he has worked with many school systems to help bring about the transition to standards-based classroom mathematics instruction in grades K–8. Dr. Rowan is a frequent presenter at NCTM and author of mathematics texts and numerous articles on teaching and learning mathematics. He currently teaches at the University of Maryland where he focuses on methods of teaching elementary school mathematics.

Kay B. Sammons

Kay Sammons is currently Elementary Mathematics Supervisor for the Howard County Public Schools in Ellicott City, Maryland, where she is responsible for curriculum and staff development for elementary teachers. She is a frequent presenter at state and national mathematics conferences. In addition to serving as a reviewer for NCTM publications, she has written textbooks and teacher resource materials. Ms. Sammons was honored as Elementary Mathematics Teacher of the Year by the Maryland Council Teachers of Mathematics and as Outstanding Educator of the Year by that same organization.

Anna R. Suarez

Anna Suarez is a national consultant and program director for K–8 Mathematics at the National Science Foundation in Arlington, Virginia. Her participation in an NSF-funded research study, Cognitively Guided Instruction (C.G.I.), helped to develop teachers' knowledge of children's mathematical thinking as the basis for making instructional decisions. She has written staff development materials for both the *Investigations* curriculum and Insight.

About the Standards

T*he Principles and Standards for School Mathematics 2000* are built around ten curriculum standards. Five of those standards address the mathematical content, or body of mathematical knowledge, that children should learn. Content standards prescribe *what* is to be taught in mathematics. The content standards are Number and Operation, Algebra, Geometry, Measurement, and Data Analysis and Probability.

The other five standards are process standards. The process standards describe *how* the content is delivered. They address how children will acquire the necessary mathematical content and how that knowledge will be applied. The five process standards are identified as Problem Solving, Reasoning and Proof, Communication, Connections, and Representation.

It should be pointed out that the content standards and process standards are not separate subsets of the whole, but are intricately interrelated. How mathematics is learned is as important as what mathematics is learned. The process standards help to "frame" how the content standards are presented.

It is possible to weave the process standards into the teaching of mathematics through a variety of methods. Children can and should be presented with meaningful problems to solve and situations that require them to reason through information to find solutions. They should be asked to defend their solutions and explain their thinking. In presenting a problem to children, connections might be made to a similar problem to build on previous learning. A representative model might be used to enhance children's understanding of a concept. Continuous communication, written and oral, will provide feedback about children's understanding.

For children to become mathematically powerful, it is essential that they be able to use process skills flexibly. They need to practice applying reasoning to solve problems and proving that their solutions are correct. They need to experiment with a variety of representations and have the ability to use them in solving problems and in illustrating their thinking. They should be able to communicate their mathematical thinking and solutions to the teacher and to other children both orally and in writing. Making connections between problems within mathematics is as essential as is making mathematical connections to disciplines outside of mathematics. The importance of how these processes interrelate and work together cannot be overemphasized.

Content Standards

Number and Operation

Algebra

Geometry

Measurement

Data Analysis and Probability

Process Standards

Problem Solving

Reasoning and Proof

Communication

Connections

Representation

Primary Problem Solving

PROBLEM SOLVING IS AT THE HEART of mathematics—it is what mathematicians do. Balance is achieved through the interrelationship of conceptual learning, basic skills, and problem solving. Developing concepts with concrete representations ensures understanding and enables students to create a strong foundation on which to build. Children need basic skills in order to apply and record their understandings with efficiency. But most importantly, they need good problems to solve, problems in which they can apply their conceptual understanding and utilize basic skills.

In its simplest form, problem solving means finding a solution when the answer is not readily apparent. Because problem solving does not always follow a uniform plan, children need to develop persistence to be able to work problems through to the end. Sometimes persistence means changing direction. *Well, we know that way doesn't work. What should we try next? Is there another way we can look at this problem?* Questions that encourage children to look for other options should be an integral part of the discussions that take place in mathematics classes.

Choosing problems that have relevance to children is an important factor in creating enthusiasm for problem solving. Often, the enthusiasm of the teacher translates into a positive disposition toward problem solving for children. If statements like "Now that's an unusual problem. I wonder how we can find the answer," are part of a teacher's repertoire, children get the notion that problem solving is interesting and they are encouraged to use their own resources to find a path to the solution.

Acquiring a variety of strategies to access for problem solving is essential to experiencing success. Having flexibility to solve problems in different ways enables children to get "unstuck" if they reach a "dead end;" it allows them to have other approaches to try. Children should be provided with instruction and practice in using a wide range of strategies that they can then draw upon.

Many young children come to school with an innate understanding of how to solve mathematical problems. The teachers' task is to build on this problem-solving ability by posing challenging problems that are accessible to all children. Fortunately, the primary classroom is full of wonderful problems for young children.

Asking thought-provoking questions to help children begin and sustain the process of solving the problem is another important role of the teacher.

- *How many days are there until Halloween? How can we find out?*
- *If we divide the class into three teams, how many children will be on each team? What can we do that will help us figure this out?*
- *If everyone gets four crackers, how many crackers will we need altogether? If a box contains 24 crackers, will one box be enough? How many boxes will we need?*
- *If we want to extend our pattern, what shape should come next? How can we find out?*

Children should be encouraged to talk with one another and share their thinking with each other as well as the teacher as they solve problems. "Two heads are better than one" is an old saying that has special meaning in the process

of problem solving. As children work together, they are able to come up with many more approaches to a problem than a child working alone would. The teacher should point out differing strategies for the solution of a problem. Children should be asked to compare the strategies to see if there are similarities and note how they differ. Children should also be asked to consider which solutions they think work best for the particular problem and why. This opens the door to a rich discussion that will broaden the learning experience for all.

Primary Reasoning and Proof

Reasoning is fundamental to the study of mathematics—it is a state of mind that causes children to explore, to justify, and to validate. It permeates all content areas and all grade levels. Children are reasoning when they interpret data, when they solve problems, and when they view geometric patterns and shapes. As they are presented with new problems, they use reasoning skills to apply previously acquired information and to test the validity of their solutions. Reasoning is the process by which children make sense of mathematics.

As they develop mathematically, children learn that mathematics is a discipline based on an inherent set of rules. Reasoning begins with intuition. This

intuition is used by even the youngest children in their efforts to make sense of mathematics, and it should be encouraged as the basis of reasoning at all grade levels. This informal intuition will become the basis for reasoning through representations that are more formal and for proofs based upon the rules.

Activities that have children compare, sort, and classify provide wonderful opportunities to develop reasoning skills. In a kindergarten classroom, children might use the buttons in a button jar and sort them by a variety of attributes. One child might place all the buttons of one color together; another might sort the buttons by the number of holes; still another by the material from which they're made, such as metal, plastic, or wood. The reasoning at this age is generally limited to one attribute. But as a child advances to first and second grade, he may be able to sort the buttons by two attributes to make a set that includes only buttons that are red and have four holes. When children explain their rules for sorting and how their choices were made, they are able to validate their thinking.

Being able to identify patterns is another prerequisite for the development of reasoning skills. A child who can recognize that the pattern is 2 hearts and 3 stars will be able to extend the pattern and to predict what shape will come next.

What are some other ways reasoning and proof can be incorporated into the mathematics class? An excellent way is by asking questions. *How did you get your answer? Tell me how you thought about that? Why does your solution work?* Questions such as these help children learn that it is important to have reasons for what they say. They also help children realize that mathematics makes sense and isn't just a system of rules and procedures to be blindly followed.

Another powerful way to develop reasoning in young children is to engage them in mathematical discussions. Piaget believed that in order for children to develop reasoning, it was imperative to have social interaction. Designating time during the mathematics lesson for discussion about their thinking allows that interaction. In any class, there will be a wide range of reasoning ability; it's helpful for children with less mature reasoning abilities to hear from those with well-developed skills. Mathematical discussions increase a child's repertoire of reasoning skills.

In a first grade class, the teacher might ask children to give the sum of $8 + 7$. When called upon, a child responds with the sum and is asked to explain how the sum was found.

- One child might explain that he got the answer by counting on his fingers and demonstrate that by physically counting eight fingers and then adding seven more.
- Another child may draw tally marks on paper to represent 8 and 7 and then show that it is equal to 15 by counting to eight and then counting on from there to fifteen.
- Another child might tell you that she knows $8 + 7 = 15$ because she can "take the two out of seven and combine it with the eight to make 10. There is 5 left over so 10 and 5 make fifteen. $8 + 7 = 8 + (2 + 5) = 10 + 5 = 15$."
- Still another student might say, "I know that $7 + 7 = 14$ and 1 more is 15."

All of these children are using what they know is true about mathematics and using mathematical reasoning to solve the problem. A child who is still counting on his fingers to get that answer will hear strategies from other children that he can begin to think about and later apply.

Working on reasoning skills and having children offer explanations of their thinking to defend their answers in the primary grades helps lay the foundation for more formal mathematical argumentation in later grades.

Primary Communication

WHETHER BETWEEN TEACHER AND CHILD, between a pair of children, or among groups of children, the communication skills of reading, writing, and listening and speaking provide the means for sharing ideas and promoting mathematical understanding. As children express their ideas through oral and written language, they have an opportunity to clarify their thinking and reinforce their own comprehension of concepts they are working with. By listening to explanations given by their classmates, children are exposed to ideas they may not have thought of. This provides a greater network of connections among ideas and, in turn, enhances learning.

Ample opportunities to discuss mathematical ideas should be provided. One extremely effective technique that was described in the previous section on Reasoning and Proof involves presenting an interesting problem to the class, allowing time to solve the problem, and then asking children to explain how they solved the problem. Providing a forum for a number of different solutions to be presented and defended by children results in rich dialogue.

There is a very high level of mental activity associated with social interaction of this nature. Children who are afforded opportunities to take part in these mathematical conversations on a regular basis learn more effectively how to reason and defend their answers. In the process, they also learn to communicate and to clarify and refine their ideas, which leads to deeper understanding.

Through discussion, children also learn to organize their mathematical thinking in order to communicate their ideas to one another. In their exchange of ideas, children naturally want to have their position make sense. Providing opportunities to present their views allows young children to articulate, clarify, organize, and consolidate their thinking. This communication enables them to reflect on what they know and demonstrate this knowledge to others.

When children are able to articulate their ideas the teacher gains insight into their thinking. For example, one kindergarten child told a teacher that he knew $5 + 2 = 8$. Because the child was able to verbalize the idea, the teacher was able to help the child modify the answer by asking him to prove the

answer using objects like Teddy Bear Counters. As the child counted 5 and 2 more, he realized that he only had 7, not 8.

Astounding language development is characteristic of the primary grades. It is important at this level that children begin to understand and use the special language of mathematics. Every opportunity to build conventional mathematical vocabulary should be taken advantage of. For example, during playtime as a child explains a shape to his friend and describes it as "the one with 4 sides," there's an opportunity for the teacher to explain that the shape is a *square*.

Putting ideas on paper also helps young children organize their thinking. The act of writing something down causes students to organize ideas and refine them before committing them to paper. Words, pictures, and numbers are all part of written communication. Journal writing, which can begin in kindergarten, helps children relate what they know about mathematics and can serve as an important tool for teachers as they assess their children's mathematical understanding.

Primary grade children should be provided with opportunities to share their mathematical ideas on a daily basis. This process is essential to internalizing mathematics.

Primary Connections

Making connections in mathematics is a three-fold process. Connections are made when one mathematical idea is used to build another; they are made among different mathematical ideas and content areas; and they are made between mathematics and contexts outside the field of mathematics.

Because mathematics is an integrated discipline, treating it as a whole body of knowledge and focusing on the connections that occur naturally adds dimension to ideas and concepts. How is counting related to addition, addition to subtraction, addition to multiplication, multiplication to area? A cohesive curriculum that is clearly articulated from pre-kindergarten through the twelfth grade, one that connects the mathematical ideas within each grade as well as the mathematics between grade levels, is critical if those connections are to take place.

Making connections to prior mathematical experiences is vital for the understanding of how mathematical ideas build on one another. Teachers need to know what mathematics children learned previously in order to build on that knowledge. In a given unit of study, attention should be paid to ensure that mathematics concepts build upon one another from day to day in a coherent manner. Teachers should also be aware of what their children will be studying in subsequent grades so they can lay the foundation for obvious connections to further studies.

Mathematics permeates other curriculum areas and it is found in the everyday experience outside of school as well. The use of shapes and patterns is prevalent in art and architecture; measurement skills and classification skills are important in science; measurement skills and knowledge of fractions are utilized in cooking and in building models; and measurement skills, data gathering, and statistics are applied in the social sciences.

Because mathematics is often integrated into other subjects at the primary level, the children do not view it as a separate study. They count the number of boys and girls in attendance at school each day. They look for patterns on the calendar and in the environment. They build with blocks, observing and communicating about the attributes of each. They sort and classify a variety of objects. They plant seeds and measure their growth.

As young children strive to make sense of their world, they naturally make connections to prior experiences. As a pre-schooler counts a group of four juice boxes on the table and says, "One, two, three, four," counting numbers are being connected with objects. The counting may be based on hearing someone else count, or the child may have had previous counting experiences and is able to transfer those experiences to this new situation. Many preschool children are not able to recite a counting number for each object they point to because they have not yet internalized one-to-one correspondence. They don't yet understand that if they count each object and end up at 4, there are 4 objects in the group. How are such connections made? Repeated experiences in the classroom where children have opportunities to count boys, girls, crayons, blocks, and so on, will ensure those connections over time.

It is important for teachers to be conscious of connections that can be made in mathematics and to weave those connections into daily practice. When children are able to connect mathematical ideas both inside and outside of the classroom, they begin to see mathematics as a cohesive body of knowledge.

Primary Representation

REPRESENTATIONS PROVIDE VEHICLES for expressing and internalizing mathematical thought. They are a critical component in shaping the way children access, understand, express, and utilize mathematical ideas. Representations include physical objects, pictures, and symbols. They also include mental images, words, and ideas.

Representations can be formal or informal. Examples of formal representations are the conventional symbols, graphs, diagrams, and so on traditionally introduced in school mathematics. More informal forms are often invented by children as a way of making sense of mathematical ideas and communicating

those ideas to classmates or the teacher. Children should be allowed to create their own understanding and explanations, and to express relationships before more conventional representations are introduced. Connecting to their invented forms will facilitate a meaningful transition to thinking and communicating in the language of mathematics.

As teachers design lessons, choosing the type of representations they feel will best help children understand a concept becomes an important consideration. What shared mathematical language is needed to effectively communicate ideas? What manipulatives or models will be appropriate? How will children record their understanding of the concept? When is it appropriate to move from physical to symbolic representation?

Consider this problem for kindergarten children.

> **A man went fishing in the morning and caught 3 fish. In the afternoon, he caught 4 more fish. How many did he catch all together?**

A kindergarten child might use counters representing the situation to help make sense of the problem.

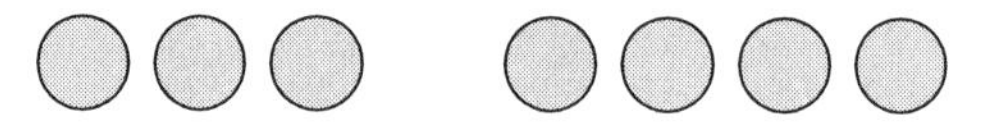

The teacher must decide when it's appropriate to move to a more formal representation of the information. By the time that child reaches second grade, there should be no difficulty representing that same problem symbolically.

$$3 + 4 = 7$$

There are multiple representations for any mathematics concept. The greater the number of ways to represent the same idea a child has knowledge of, the greater the flexibility available in solving problems. For example, the number 25 can be thought of as 2 tens and 5 ones; the same as a quarter; halfway between 1 and 50; an odd number; one more than 24; five less than 30; 12 + 13; and so on. A child with access to this variety of representations of 25 is able to choose which version is useful for a particular situation.

One way to successfully build multiple representations for a number with young children is to feature a number each day in the classroom. Begin the math period by presenting a number for the day, such as 18, and ask children to find as many ways as they can to make that number. This activity is one that all children can work on, and it will increase their ability to think flexibly. Here are some names for 18 found by a second grader.

18 + 0	17 + 1	9 + 9
16 + 2	9 x 2	20 − 2
6 + 6 + 6	10 + 8	22 − 4
5 + 5 + 5 + 3	10 + 10 − 2	9 + 8 + 1

1+1+1+1+1+1+1+1+1+1+1+1+1+1+1+1+1+1

To begin with, children record their mathematical ideas in very personal ways. As they continue their mathematical growth, they are introduced to conventional representations. Both forms of representation are powerful tools for understanding and communicating abstract ideas.

Conclusion

The process standards are not an end in, and of, themselves. Rather, they provide the advanced organizers or plan for lessons that present important mathematics content. Seeing connections among mathematical topics enables children to reason and make sense of new ideas and problem-solving situations they encounter. Through the process of communication, children are able to represent these new ideas either formally or informally.

Just as the process standards are interrelated, so are the process and content standards. For true mathematical thinking and learning to occur, both process and content need to be skillfully woven into and through each lesson. That is the goal to work toward.

Standard 1 **Number and Operation**

AT THE FIRST GRADE LEVEL, number and operation includes children relating the numeral, written word, developing strategies for adding two or three numbers, and introducing children to the idea of skip counting. Our lessons are derived from these important topics, and include a lesson on recognizing the numerals, written words, and dot patterns for the numbers one through six, a lesson that teaches the commutative strategy for addition facts in which one or two is the first addend, a lesson that teaches children to look for combinations that make ten when adding three numbers, and a lesson that introduces children to skip counting by twos, fives, and tens.

Three lessons model how the process standards can be used to teach content. A fourth lesson is a hypothetical textbook lesson that we have revised to be more standards based. These four lessons do not represent the entire curriculum, but rather provide glimpses of how, with a more concentrated effort to incorporate the process standards, better mathematics teaching and learning can be achieved.

One lesson we have chosen relates numerals, written words, and dot patterns for the numbers one through six. The process standards representation and connections are the basis for this lesson as children make connections among the three different representations of each number.

Another lesson we have chosen focuses on using the commutative property as a strategy for adding two numbers when the first addend is 1 or 2. Children have used the counting on strategy when the second addend is 1 or 2. Now, through reasoning and proof and different representations, children will come to realize that switching the order of two addends does not change the sum. The addend 1 or 2 can always be the second addend, and the counting on strategy can be used.

A third lesson we have chosen is one that suggests a strategy for adding three numbers—to look for a pair of numbers that add to 10, then add the third number. The process standard reasoning and proof propels this lesson. Children write the six ways in which three addends may be added, notice that the sum is always the same, and are asked to decide which of the ways was the easiest or most efficient.

The hypothetical textbook lesson we have chosen to revise introduces children to skip counting by twos, fives, and tens. Through the process standards of representation and connections, children begin to see the usefulness of being able to skip count in their daily experiences. They also develop ways to learn and remember the skip-counting patterns.

Standard 1 Lessons

Connecting Numerals and Number Words

Using the Commutative Strategy

Recognizing Ten

Investigating Number Patterns: Skip Counting

Connecting Numerals and Number Words

Introduction

Objective → Children will match numerals with written words and with dot patterns and will write the words for the numbers one through six.

Context → Children have learned to count by ones and understand cardinality. They will use their knowledge of numbers and number words to establish ordinal sequence.

NCTM Standards Focus

In this standards-based lesson, children concentrate on developing strategies for connecting number words to numerals and quantity. They are allowed to explore and make their own connections. In doing this, they are able to focus explicitly on what they learned in one situation and then apply it to other situations. This enables them to start developing a bank of strategies that they can use in other learning situations.

Connections Children make connections between counting, quantity, and written number words. They connect numerals and number words to numerical order.

Representation Children represent quantities in three different ways: as numerals, as dot patterns, and as number words. They also represent numerals and number words by drawing a number of objects that correspond to the numeral and number word.

Teaching Plan

Materials → Student pages 22–23; crayons

BEGIN THE LESSON BY DRAWING one dot on the board or overhead and ask children to tell how many dots there are. Then have a volunteer write the numeral. *What is the same about the dot and the numeral? What do both show?* Write the word "one" below the dot and the numeral. *How many ways has "one" been represented?* Write "one" again, saying each letter as you write it.

Give each child student page 22. Have them find the numeral 1, represent it with dots, and write the numeral word by tracing the letters next to the numeral. Repeat the entire activity for the numerals 2 through 6. As children work, make sure that they make the connection between the numeral, the number of dots, and the corresponding number word.

3 • • • three

This activity strongly incorporates the representations and connections that motivate this lesson. Children see three representations of a number on the board, and strengthen their connections between the different forms. Children are not always presented the opportunity to see all three forms together.

WRITE THE NUMBER WORDS from page 22 on the board or on the overhead before giving children student page 23. Ask them to read the words with you in unison. You might want to do this a few times as well as have volunteers read the words to the class.

Direct the children's attention to student page 23. Discuss the first numeral. *What quantity does the numeral represent? How many dots will represent the numeral? What number word represents the numeral?* Ask one of the children to draw the number of dots that represents the quantity "four" and then write the number word. Have children count the number of dots aloud and then say the letters aloud that are in the number word "four." Ask them to explain how they know how many dots to use for each number. Then ask how they can figure out what word to write for each numeral.

What Children Might Say

- To figure out how many dots to write, they can say the numeral aloud and then count as they draw that many dots.
- They then say the number word for the numeral aloud and listen for the initial sound. When they say the word for the numeral "4," they can hear that the initial sound is "f."
- They then compare the two number words that begin with the "f" sound. They can hear that "five" has an "i" sound in it, while "four" has an "o" sound in it.
- Finally, they can hear that "four" ends with an "r" sound and "five" does not. If they need to, they can then look at the number words they have learned to write to remember how to write the number "four."

CONTINUE WITH directed questioning for all the numerals on the page. Discuss each numeral and the quantity it represents. Then talk about how to draw the number of dots that show that quantity and how to write the matching number word. Remind the children that before they write the word for each numeral, they should represent the numeral with dots or circles. Again, these activities emphasize the representations and connections that are the focus of this lesson.

Children often rely on the beginning and ending sounds of the number word to figure out what to write. For example, since they have already used "four" to represent the first numeral on the page, they will probably quickly figure out that the word "five," the only other number word from 1 to 6 that begins with an "f" sound, corresponds to "5." The next two numerals on the page begin with a "t," but some children will find it difficult to discern that the "th" sound begins with a "t." For these numerals, children can use the ending sounds to distinguish the words. They can hear the long "e" sound in the word "three," and most will know that the "oo" sound in the word "two" is given by the letter "o."

"One" and "six" are sufficiently different from the other words and from each other that most children will have little or no difficulty placing the correct number word with the numeral. Throughout the writing of the number words, observe how the children approach the process of deciphering the words and writing them on the page.

When everyone has completed student page 23, make a class number book. Ask each child to choose one numeral from the student page and copy the numeral and the number word on a piece of paper. Ask children to represent their numeral by drawing a corresponding number of objects on the paper. Encourage them to be creative in deciding what to draw. You might bring in some counting books to give children ideas for illustrating their pages.

Call on children randomly to place their numerals in front of the class in order from 1 through 6. As they place their numbers, ask them to explain how they figured out where to put their number.

Combine children's drawings into a class number book. Go through the book with the children, asking them to point out the different representations of numbers.

What Might Happen . . . What to Do

Some children might need more experience with written words, sight vocabulary, or initial sounds in order to distinguish different number words. Have them use student page 22 as a guide, since the correct match of numeral/number word has already been established. If some children have difficulties forming the letters, write number words on cards for them to paste next to the numerals.

Student Pages

On student page 22, children show each number with dots and trace the number words that correspond to each numeral. On student page 23, children represent each numeral with dots and then write the correct number word for each numeral.

Assessment

During the activities in this lesson, you had the opportunity to assess how children matched numerals with quantity when they represented numerals with dots. You then observed how well they determined which number word matched each numeral and quantity. You were able to assess the strategies they used for matching number words and numerals and for reading and writing number words.You could see through the explanations of their work whether they understood the connections between numerals, quantities, and number words. You could also begin to see whether they understood the concept of ordering numbers.

NCTM Standards Summary

Children made connections between the numerals 1 through 6, the corresponding written number words, and the quantity each numeral and word expresses. They also connected these numerals and number words to numerical order. They used their knowledge of reading to figure out number words and then connected their knowledge of counting to reading. Children represented quantities as numerals, dot patterns, and number words. They also represented each numeral and number word with objects in a class number book.

Answers

Page 23

4	• • • •	four
5	• • • • •	five
2	• •	two
3	• • •	three
1	•	one
6	• • • • • •	six

Name

Connecting Numerals and Number Words

Show each number with dots. Trace each number word.

1  one

2 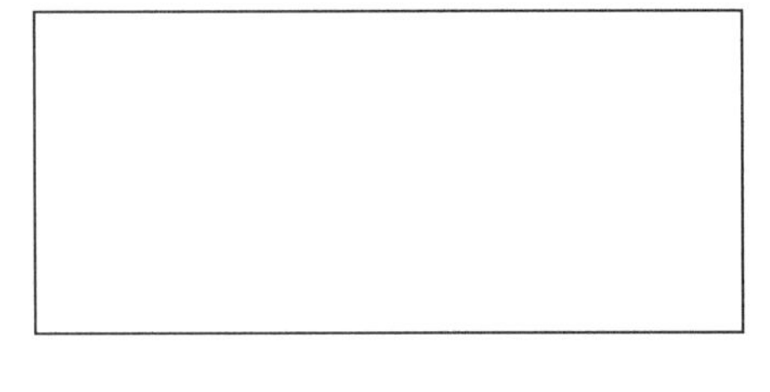 two

3 three

4 four

5  five

6  six

Name ______________________

Connecting Numerals and Number Words

Show each number with dots. Then write the number word.

4

____

5

____

2

____

3

____

1

____

____

Using the Commutative Strategy

Introduction

Objective → Children will use the commutative property and counting on to solve addition problems in which one of the addends is 1 or 2.

Context → Children have counted objects and pictures using one-to-one correspondence with numbers to 100. They have used addition and subtraction sentences with numbers to 10. In future lessons, children will subtract subtrahends of 1 and 2 by counting back.

NCTM Standards Focus

When children are allowed to explore an important concept like the commutative property, they are actively involved and prove to themselves that the commutative property holds true in different situations. From this, they can generalize that it holds true for adding in general. Children are often presented the commutative property without an opportunity to think about it or explore it for themselves.

Reasoning and Proof Children verify to themselves and classmates that the commutative property applies to the addition problems in this lesson.

Connections Children make connections between counting, addition with 1 or 2 as addends, and commutative addition problems. They also make connections between counting and adding on a number line.

Representation Children represent addition sentences with 1 or 2 as addends using concrete materials and symbolic representation on a number line.

Teaching Plan

Materials → Student pages 28–29; counters

DISTRIBUTE STUDENT PAGE 28. Draw a similar number line on the board or overhead.

Write the number sentence $8 + 1 = \square$. Ask the child to show the number sentence on the number line, and the answer. Then have children model other number sentences from the first column on the page. *What do you notice about adding 1 to a number?* Children might say that when they add 1 to a number, it is like counting, since it is the next number.

What Might Happen . . . What to Do

Some children might first count up to 8 by ones and then count 1 more. Discuss with them how they can eliminate the step of counting up to the first number. Encourage them to begin at 8 and then count 1 more. Do several examples like this, making the first addend greater each time to discourage children from counting up to the addend.

Reverse the addends and have children do $1 + 8 = \square$ on the number line. Have them share what they notice. Continue with other number sentences in the second column of student page 28. Observe when children no longer rely on the number line. Ask them to describe what they have noticed about the order of the addends. (Changing the order of the addends does not change the answer.)

Give children some further examples with greater addends, such as $1 + 28$ and $1 + 43$. Observe whether they apply the commutative property to these problems by asking them in which order they added the numbers and why. Ask them how confident they were that they would obtain the correct answer.

Continue the lesson using the same number sentences, but this time have children add 2 instead of 1. Present the number sentence $8 + 2 = \square$. Point out 8 on the number line, then count on 2.

What Might Happen . . . What to Do

Some children might count on from 8 by saying 8, 9. Draw a circle or place a transparent counter on the number, and count on from 8, saying 9, 10. Emphasize that counting on means adding 1 more or 2 more, so that starting with 8, 1 more is 9 and 2 more is 10.

Have children complete the number sentences on student page 28. Using the number line, encourage children to either circle the first addend or place a counter on it and count on from the marked number. After they have completed the activity, ask them what they can say about adding 2 to a number.

What Children Might Say

- Adding 2 to a number is like adding 1 and then another 1 to the first number.
- When adding 2 to a number, skip the next number and go to the following number.
- You can use skip counting by 2 to add two to a number, especially when the first addend is an even number.

REVERSE THE ADDENDS AGAIN and have children work individually to predict the sums without using the number line. Show them the remaining number sentences from student page 28, $2 + 8 = \square$, $2 + 9 = \square$, $2 + 16 = \square$, $2 + 19 = \square$, and $2 + 23 = \square$, and ask them to write the sums.

Ask children to prove that their predicted sums are correct by using the number line. When the children are finished, have them share what they noticed. Children should notice that the answers are the same as from the problems in the left column. It does not matter in which order you add 1 or 2 to a number—either order gives you the same answer.

Extension

Give the children number sentences using one addend greater than 30 and the other addend 1 or 2, such as $55 + 1 = \square$ and $55 + 2 = \square$. Encourage them to solve the addition problems mentally and then have them check the results using a calculator. Reverse the addends and have children tell or write how they know the answers.

Student Pages

Student page 28 provides a number line and lists the number sentences the children will use during the lesson. Student page 29 contains practice problems. You might have children use this page at the end of the exploratory part of the lesson or send it home for homework.

Assessment

During the lesson you had the chance to observe how children approached counting on by 1 or 2 and related this to addition. You were also able to assess whether they recognized that the order in which they added numbers did not matter. As you review your assessment of the children's progress, keep in mind whether they have grasped the commutative property.

NCTM Standards Summary

Children verified that the commutative property applied to the addition problems that they solved. By reversing addends and using a number line, children proved that changing the order of the addends does not change the answer. They made connections between counting, addition with 1 or 2 as addends, and commutative addition problems. Children represented addition sentences by using a number line and generalized about the order in which numbers are added.

Answers

Page 28

1. 9
2. 9
3. 10
4. 10
5. 17
6. 17
7. 20
8. 20
9. 24
10. 24
11. 10
12. 10
13. 11
14. 11
15. 18
16. 18
17. 21
18. 21
19. 25
20. 25

Page 29

1. 6
2. 6
3. 11
4. 11
5. 9
6. 9
7. 15
8. 15
9. 12
10. 12
11. 24
12. 24
13. 20
14. 20
15. 30
16. 30
17. 16
18. 16
19. 27
20. 27

Name ______________________________

Using the Commutative Strategy

Use the number line to solve each problem. Show how you added.

1. 8 + 1 = ______
2. 1 + 8 = ______
3. 9 + 1 = ______
4. 1 + 9 = ______
5. 16 + 1 = ______
6. 1 + 16 = ______
7. 19 + 1 = ______
8. 1 + 19 = ______
9. 23 + 1 = ______
10. 1 + 23 = ______

---

11. 8 + 2 = ______
12. 2 + 8 = ______
13. 9 + 2 = ______
14. 2 + 9 = ______
15. 16 + 2 = ______
16. 2 + 16 = ______
17. 19 + 2 = ______
18. 2 + 19 = ______
19. 23 + 2 = ______
20. 2 + 23 = ______

Name ____________________

Using the Commutative Strategy

Add. Show how you added.

1. 5 + 1 = ______
2. 1 + 5 = ______
3. 10 + 1 = ______
4. 1 + 10 = ______
5. 7 + 2 = ______
6. 2 + 7 = ______
7. 13 + 2 = ______
8. 2 + 13 = ______
9. 11 + 1 = ______
10. 1 + 11 = ______
11. 22 + 2 = ______
12. 2 + 22 = ______
13. 18 + 2 = ______
14. 2 + 18 = ______
15. 29 + 1 = ______
16. 1 + 29 = ______
17. 14 + 2 = ______
18. 2 + 14 = ______
19. 26 + 1 = ______
20. 1 + 26 = ______

Recognizing Ten

Introduction

Objective → Children will find the sums of three addends by recognizing two addends that make 10.

Context → Children have learned addition facts and added 10 to a number. They will go on to learn to subtract 10 and near-10 and to explore the relationship between addition and subtraction by creating fact families.

NCTM Standards Focus

Recognizing 10 is the basis for understanding place value. When children explore the importance of making 10 when adding three addends, they experience the efficiency of the base 10 system. Research shows that children begin to understand place value only when they form their own ideas about it and actively experience it. By focusing on the process standards of reasoning and proof, connections, and communication, this is exactly what children do in this lesson.

Reasoning and Proof Children make and verify predictions about finding the sum of three addends. Building on these predictions, they devise effective strategies for finding the sums of three addends.

Connections Children make informal connections to the commutative and associative properties of addition. They also connect to their prior knowledge of addition, math facts, and combinations that make 10 to add three numbers.

Communication Children explain the strategies they used to add three addends and discuss as a class the conclusions or generalizations they can make about adding three addends.

Teaching Plan

Materials → Student pages 34–35; counters

ARRANGE THE CHILDREN IN PAIRS and tell them that they will play a math game. Pass out one copy of student page 34 to each pair and have the children cut out the addition cards. One partner shuffles and deals the cards. Children then take turns holding up cards for their partners to solve. When a child correctly solves a problem, he/she keeps the card and sets it aside. If the partner does not know the sum, the child who showed it gets a chance to answer. At the end, the partner with the most cards wins. Observe children as they play the game, paying attention to recall of the tens facts and adding 10 to a number.

ASK THE CHILDREN TO LIST all the math facts that make 10. Write them on the board or overhead. Begin the list with $1 + 9$ or $9 + 1$ and have children tell which fact would come next in an ordered list. This will help children to prepare for the upcoming activity.

Distribute 20 counters to the same pairs of children. Ask them to solve the problem $6 + 3 + 7 =$ ____. Children could use the counters to make groups of 6, 3, and 7, and then count to find the total, or they might use their knowledge of addition facts to find the sum.

Now ask the children to solve $7 + 6 + 3 =$ ____. Observe their methods. Children will likely rearrange the groups of counters, then some might count by ones while others will recognize that the sum must be the same.

Once it has been established that the answer is the same, ask children how many other ways the three addends can be arranged. Have them record the different ways. *How many ways are there? What is the sum each time?*

As children work, assess how they group and organize the addends. Observe whether they know when they have made all the possible combinations of the three addends. When they are finished, have them share their results. Children should notice the following:

- There are 6 possible combinations of these addends.
- The sum remains the same no matter which way they combine the numbers.

CONTINUE THE LESSON BY PRESENTING a new problem, $2 + 5 + 8 =$ ____. *How many ways can these three addends be arranged?* (6) *What do you know about the sum in each case?* (It will be the same.)

Have children find the sum, but now ask them to consider which of the six ways makes the addition faster and easier. Assess the reasoning and strategies they use as they work. Notice whether they are using tens facts to solve the problem quickly.

f.y.i.

Informal connections are made here to the commutative and associative properties of addition.

Associative property—Three or more addends can be regrouped without changing the sum.

Commutative property—The sum of two given addends remains the same no matter how the addends are ordered.

Have a brief class discussion in which children explain how they solved the problem. Make sure that the method of using tens facts is mentioned and discuss how using this method makes solving problems easier. Complete the lesson by having children list the conclusions or generalizations they can make about adding with three addends.

- Each time there are three different addends, there are 6 possible ways to group them.
- The sum of the same three addends remains the same no matter how the addends are combined.
- Using tens facts can make adding easier. Before adding, check to see if some of the numbers can be combined to make 10.
- Combine numbers to make 10 first, then add the last number.

Extension

Give the children problems with five addends in which two pairs of addends each add to make 10. Ask them to show the order in which they combined the addends. Have them write about their methods.

$1 + 7 + 6 + 9 + 3 =$ ___ (26)

$1 + 7 + 8 + 3 + 2 =$ ___ (21)

$8 + 4 + 5 + 5 + 2 =$ ___ (24)

$5 + 2 + 4 + 5 + 6 =$ ___ (22)

$4 + 3 + 6 + 8 + 7 =$ ___ (28)

$9 + 8 + 5 + 2 + 1 =$ ___ (25)

Student Pages

Student page 34 contains the addition cards for children to use during the lesson. Student page 35 contains practice problems that may be assigned for homework/individual practice.

Assessment

Your observations of the methods children used to combine three addends and to find their sum, along with their discussion of those methods, enabled you to assess whether they understood how to use addition properties and tens facts to solve problems. Class discussion of the strategies they used and the conclusions they drew gave you additional insight into children's progress. The exercises on student page 35 can help you assess each child's individual progress.

NCTM Standards Summary

As they worked together, children used reasoning and proof to generalize that the sum of three addends remains the same regardless of the order in which the addends are combined. Children made connections between tens facts and adding three numbers and learned to group two addends to make 10 before adding the third addend. They also connected what they knew about the commutative property with two addends to adding with three addends and began to informally use the associative property as they regrouped addends. In class discussion, children communicated their conclusions or generalizations about adding three addends.

Answers

Page 35

Possible answers are given.

1. $1 + 9 + 3 = 13$
2. $9 + 1 + 8 = 18$
3. $4 + 6 + 5 = 15$
4. $8 + 2 + 7 = 17$
5. $3 + 7 + 3 = 13$
6. $6 + 4 + 9 = 19$
7. $9 + 1 + 9 = 19$
8. $6 + 4 + 2 = 12$
9. Answers will vary.

Name

Recognizing Ten

Cut out the addition cards.

1 + 9	2 + 8	3 + 7	4 + 6
5 + 5	9 + 1	8 + 2	7 + 3
6 + 4	10 + 0	10 + 1	10 + 2
10 + 3	10 + 4	10 + 5	10 + 6
10 + 7	10 + 8	10 + 9	10 + 10

Name ______________________

Recognizing Ten

Add. Rewrite the problem to show how you added.

Example: $7 + 5 + 3 = 7 + 3 + 5 = 15$

1. $1 + 3 + 9 =$ ___ + ___ + ___ = ___

2. $9 + 8 + 1 =$ ___ + ___ + ___ = ___

3. $4 + 5 + 6 =$ ___ + ___ + ___ = ___

4. $8 + 7 + 2 =$ ___ + ___ + ___ = ___

5. $3 + 3 + 7 =$ ___ + ___ + ___ = ___

6. $6 + 9 + 4 =$ ___ + ___ + ___ = ___

7. $9 + 9 + 1 =$ ___ + ___ + ___ = ___

8. $2 + 6 + 4 =$ ___ + ___ + ___ = ___

9. Choose 1 problem. Write about how you added and tell why.

____

____

Investigating Number Patterns: Skip Counting

Introduction

Objective → Children will skip count by 2s, 5s, and 10s.

Context → Children have experienced a wide range of counting activities prior to this lesson. Follow-up lessons may include skip-counting activities with calculators.

Name ______________

Investigating Number Patterns: Skip Counting

Learn

What happens when you go up the stairs two at a time?

How would you count the stairs?

Another way to count is to skip count.

2	4	6	8

Use the counters to skip count.
Make groups in each of the boxes. Write the numbers.

Try

1. Count by twos.

____ ____ ____ ____

2. Count by threes.

____ ____ ____ ____

3. Count by tens.

____ ____ ____ ____

Look over your work. Which numbers did you skip each time?

NCTM Process Standards Analysis and Focus

The standards analysis examines how the process standards have been incorporated into the above lesson. By increasing the focus on three of the process standards, a more effective and meaningful lesson can be presented. The suggestions offered can help you to think about how this might be accomplished.

Representation The lesson has children color in number boxes to correspond to skip-counted numbers. Children also use counters to complete worksheet activities.

Suggestion → **Provide opportunities for children to practice skip counting using a variety of models. Include concrete, auditory, and graphic representations of skip counting. These experiences will encourage**

Name ______________________

Practice

1. **Skip count by tens.**
Use a red crayon to color the numbers you counted.

1	2	3	4	5	6	7	8	9	10
11	12	13	14	15	16	17	18	19	20
21	22	23	24	25	26	27	28	29	30

2. **Skip count by threes.**
Use a blue crayon to color the numbers you counted.

1	2	3	4	5	6	7	8	9	10
11	12	13	14	15	16	17	18	19	20
21	22	23	24	25	26	27	28	29	30

More Practice

3. **Solve by skip counting.** There are five apples in each group.
How many apples are in six groups? ____________

  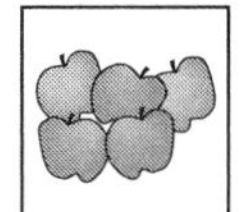 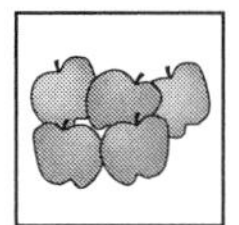  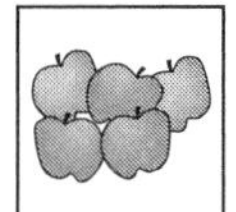

___ ___ ___ ___ ___ ___

children to look for, listen to, and remember number patterns.

Connections Children are instructed to place counters in groups, count by the number in each group, and connect the written numeral to their counting.

Suggestion → **Encourage children to look for patterns that exist when counting by specified numbers. Promote mathematical connections by having children think about everyday items that come in groups and why it would make sense to skip count.**

Communication Opportunities to discuss understanding of skip counting are limited in this lesson. Children demonstrate their understanding by recording answers and coloring boxes.

Suggestion → **Offer numerous opportunities for children to discuss their ideas about how and why skip counting is important. As examples are examined, have them skip count to determine how many. These experiences will help clarify children's understandings of the mathematical concept.**

Reasoning and Proof Examples that show how and why skip counting may be beneficial are not explored.

Problem Solving The lesson's purpose is to develop a basic understanding of skip counting. Problem solving is not involved.

The teaching plan that follows shows how the suggestions for increasing the focus on the process standards can be implemented.

Revised Teaching Plan

Materials → Chart paper; number line; 1 hundred chart per children pair; counters

Teaching the Lesson

ASK FIVE TO EIGHT VOLUNTEERS to line up in front of the classroom. *How many ears do you think there are in this line? Let's check.* Walk behind each child as you lightly place your hands over their ears. Invite children to join you as you count aloud by 2s. Repeat the counting, only this time record the number pattern—2, 4, 6, 8, and so on—on chart paper as you count. This will enable children to see the counting pattern in written form.

REPEAT THE ACTIVITY to skip count children's eyes. Encourage children to count along with you. *Why count by 2s rather than count each eye separately? How is counting by 2s helpful?* Have children predict what number will come next when another child is added to the line. Check and confirm their predictions. Continue adding children as correct responses are given. Children will see that while not every object is counted individually, each is included in the *total* count. These concrete experiences demonstrate how skip counting actually includes numbers that are not counted aloud.

Repeat a similar activity with other volunteers. First, work with children to skip count by 5s (children can raise a hand or lift a foot while seated) and then by 10s (children can show both hands or lift both feet while seated). Discuss the importance of skip counting to clarify children's understandings.

BRAINSTORM AND CHART REAL-WORLD EXAMPLES for skip counting, such as counting pairs of shoes, six packs of juice, and cartons of eggs. *Why does it make sense to count by different numbers at different times? Can you think of other examples?*

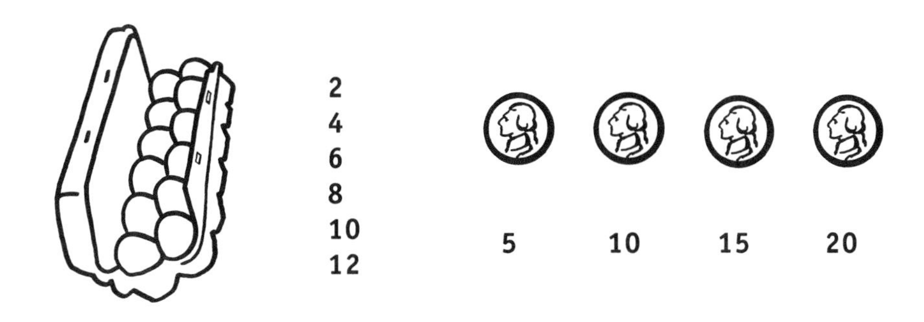

f.y.i.

Help children make real-world connections for skip counting by using nickels or dimes for skip-counting activities. Money offers an immediate way for children to see the relevance of skip counting in their world.

Use a large number line to reinforce skip counting with a visual model. Begin by counting by 2s. Draw arrows to mark each number as you count aloud. This visual representation will help children see which numbers are skipped. *Did you notice how many numbers we skipped on the number line each time we counted by 2s? Let's check.* This type of question helps children both see and internalize number patterns. List children's observations on chart paper to reinforce their understandings: when you count by 2s, you skip one number; when you count by 5s, you skip four numbers; and when you count by 10s, you skip nine numbers.

Model another representation for skip counting by clapping out a number pattern. Ask children to listen as you clap and encourage them to join in when they know the pattern. Quietly clap your hands together either one, four, or nine times. Then lift your hands up on the 2nd, 5th, or 10th clap respectively. When most children have joined in with the pattern, have a volunteer use a pointer to show the pattern on the number line. Gradually begin to count softly as you clap and loudly when you raise your hands to place emphasis on the numbers. Vary the activity to emphasize counting by 2s, 5s, or 10s.

Distribute modified hundred charts to pairs of children. Hundred charts provide a context for children to note and talk about patterns. Have children select three different-color crayons and include a key on the chart that represents their color choices for counting by 2s, 5s, and 10s. If necessary, children can place different-color counters on the hundred chart to help keep track of the number patterns. If time permits, have partners discuss the patterns found on their hundred chart. A brief discussion will reinforce the relationships that exist in skip counting and help children remember numbers. Allow time for children to share how skip counting can help them count large sets of objects faster. Point out that skip counting is another way to count and that it speeds up the counting process.

f.y.i.

Modify hundred charts according to children's counting abilities. Cut off rows from the chart to meet the needs of your children. Consider modified charts of 40, 60, or 80.

1	2	3	4	5	6	7	8	9	10
11	12	13	14	15	16	17	18	19	20
21	22	23	24	25	26	27	28	29	30
31	32	33	34	35	36	37	38	39	40
41	42	43	44	45	46	47	48	49	50
51	52	53	54	55	56	57	58	59	60
61	62	63	64	65	66	67	68	69	70
71	72	73	74	75	76	77	78	79	80
81	82	83	84	85	86	87	88	89	90
91	92	93	94	95	96	97	98	99	100

What Might Happen . . . What to Do

Children may be confused as to which numbers they should color on the hundred chart. As they skip count, remind them to skip one number fewer than the number they are counting by. For example, when skip counting by 5s, children should skip only four numbers.

Demonstrate how to count 1, 2, 3, 4, and place a counter on the next number, 5. Have children repeat 1, 2, 3, 4, and place a marker on the next number, 10. Allow time for children to color the spaces when all the counters are placed on the chart.

PROVIDE ADDITIONAL ACTIVITIES for children to use skip counting throughout the school day. Have them count by 2s, 5s, or 10s as they line up for lunch or as a bridge between activities.

Student Pages

Children are now ready to complete exercises similar to those shown on the reduced student pages.

Assessment

Clapping number patterns and using the number line offered a context in which to informally assess children's understanding of skip counting. Listening to children as they worked together with a partner to complete the hundred chart provided insight about their understanding.

NCTM Standards Summary

The lesson provided concrete, auditory, and graphic representations to help children develop the concept of skip counting. These experiences provided opportunities for children to look for, listen to, and thereby remember number patterns. Number-line activities offered a graphic representation of number patterns associated with skip counting. Clapping number patterns added another dimension to the skip-counting activity. Working with the hundred chart challenged children to look for and discuss emerging patterns. Throughout the lesson, children were encouraged to use their knowledge of numbers and number patterns to make connections to real-world experiences. Whole-class as well as partner activities promoted communication as children counted numbers and shared counting strategies with the teacher and other classmates.

Standard 2 **Algebra**

AT THE FIRST GRADE LEVEL, algebra includes work with patterns, equality, and representing and solving problems. Our lessons are derived from these important topics, and include a lesson on extending patterns, a lesson on understanding equality, a lesson that focuses on how to represent a problem, and a lesson on deciding what operation to use to solve a problem.

Three lessons model how the process standards can be used to teach content. A fourth lesson is a hypothetical textbook lesson that we have revised to be more standards based. These four lessons do not represent the entire curriculum, but rather provide glimpses of how, with a more concentrated effort to incorporate the process standards, better mathematics teaching and learning can be achieved.

In one lesson we have chosen, children recognize and extend patterns. Children also find a second way to represent a given pattern. Reasoning and proof and communication are also important here as children need chances to discuss their thinking about how to identify, extend, and recreate the patterns.

Another lesson we have chosen helps children develop a conceptual understanding of equality. Through the process standards of representation, communication, and connections, children express equality in different ways in contexts that are already familiar to them.

A third lesson we have chosen focuses children's attention on how to represent problem situations so that they can be solved. Through the process standards of representation, problem-solving, and connections, children model problem situations with manipulatives, pictures, and language. Children use their representations to solve addition and subtraction problems.

The hypothetical textbook lesson we have chosen to revise is one that has children deciding whether to use addition or subtraction to solve given problems. With better problem-solving situations and opportunities for discussion, children can learn about more clues that can help them to decide which operation to use to solve a problem. Allowing children to use manipulatives to represent and model the problem situation can also help.

Standard 2 Lessons

- **Extending Patterns**
- **Understanding Equality**
- **Representing Problems**
- **Choosing the Operation**

Extending Patterns

Introduction

Objective → Children will recognize, extend, and compare patterns.

Context → Children have made kinesthetic and geometric shape patterns. In future lessons, they will use numerical patterns in addition and subtraction.

NCTM Standards Focus

In this standards-based lesson, children recognize and extend patterns that involve color, shape, or numbers. They work on generalizing their knowledge about patterns by making rules for writing patterns and then making patterns. They also try to determine when a sequence of objects or numbers is not a pattern.

Reasoning and Proof Children make and verify predictions about patterns. They use reasoning to show how some patterns that they are familiar with are similar to new patterns with letters and numbers.

Communication Children explain to one another how given patterns are similar and how they are different. They share how they found the rule for patterns, how they extended patterns, how they made their predictions, and how they confirmed these predictions.

Representation Children will study patterns through their representations and determine the pattern rule. Children will extend their patterns through representation.

Teaching Plan

Materials → Student pages 48–49; tiles of two different colors (red and yellow are used in the lesson); attribute blocks

BEGIN THE LESSON by telling children that today they will be working with patterns. Provide children with color tiles. You may want them to work in pairs or individually depending on how many materials you have. Show them a red, yellow, red, yellow pattern. Ask children what they think the pattern is. Have them tell why they think that is the pattern. Ask them to make the original pattern and then extend the pattern for four more tiles. Encourage children to discuss what they did and why.

Ask children to look at their patterns and tell you what the 3rd tile is, the 5th, and so on. Then ask children to tell you what the 10th tile would be and how they know.

What Might Happen . . . What to Do

Some children might not have had many experiences with patterning. Create an AB pattern by repeating the pattern rule three times. Have children tell the colors in the pattern one at a time. Ask children what part repeats and have them identify it. It is important that children take a minute to focus on what part repeats. You may even want children to put straws or some other divider between the parts that repeat. Repeat this activity several times using different colors.

f.y.i.

It is important when demonstrating patterns, to show at least two full cycles of the pattern. Children need to see the two full cycles to determine what is repeating. If they do not see the two full cycles, they can only guess at what is repeating.

Give children attribute blocks. Make sure they have the same thickness. Create a pattern using the same color but different shapes. You may choose, for example, small rectangle, small triangle, small rectangle, small triangle, small rectangle, small triangle. *What will the next shape be? How do you know?* Then, use small rectangles and small squares to make another AB pattern. Ask children questions about how to extend the pattern.

How is this pattern like the one we made with tiles? How is it different? Children should be able to point out that one pattern focused on two different colors, while the shape was the same. The other pattern alternated two different shapes, while the color remained the same.

Have children predict the shape of the tenth attribute block and then prove or disprove that their prediction is correct. Ask them about the twelfth attribute block. This question is a good one because some children might recognize that they really don't have to extend the pattern because they know the tenth and twelfth items would be the same.

Now tell children that soon they will be making their own patterns, but before they do, the class is going to make a list of things to think about when making patterns.

USE THE BOARD or overhead. Tell children that you will write down the ideas that everyone agrees on to help them when they make their own patterns. The most important thing for children to see is that in a pattern there is a part of the sequence that repeats. If children share an idea that is not correct, let the class consider it for a minute. If no one points out the error, give an example to counter the proposed rule. Ask if your sequence fits with what children talked about earlier in the lesson, and whether or not it could be a pattern. Make sure children understand that your counter example shows a pattern since it shows a segment that repeats and shows only repeating segments.

What Might Happen . . . What to Do

Some children may have trouble creating patterns. Often they have a pattern in their heads, but don't know how to show it on paper. Give these children more experiences with patterns that you provide. Ask them to circle each segment of the pattern that repeats. This activity will reinforce the idea that a pattern is made up of repeating segments only—there are no "extra" parts. When children move on to making their own patterns, have them continue to circle the repeating elements in the patterns until you are confident that the children understand the patterning concept.

f.y.i.

Although it is important to use concrete materials, you might also want to have children draw their predictions on grid paper. They can then use these drawings when called upon to prove their predictions.

Use the board or overhead. Tell children that now they will play a game called "Do You See a Pattern?" Explain that you will show them what may be a pattern or what may not be a pattern. Using attribute blocks or drawings, show children various sequences—some patterns, some not patterns. As you display each sequence, also use the letters A and B to label each item in the pattern. Some samples are provided below. Tell the children that when they know whether or not the sequence shows a pattern they should fold their hands on their desks. Then when you ask them to tell you whether or not the sequence is a pattern, they should show thumbs up for "yes" and thumbs down for "no." Be sure that you always discuss why the sequence does or doesn't show a pattern.

- ABAAAB; No
- BABABA; Yes
- AABABAB;No
- AB; No

Now assign the student pages. You may want to work through the pages in class.

Student Pages

Student page 48 contains grids for children to make patterns and answer questions about them. Page 49 has questions about different patterns.

Assessment

During the class discussion there were opportunities to assess children's understanding of patterns and pattern rules. The "Do You See a Pattern Game?" gave an opportunity to judge their understanding since you can see all children's responses at once. Both student pages gave insights into children's understanding.

NCTM Standards Summary

Children built on their early understanding of patterns to extend and predict patterns. They used reasoning to predict which component of the pattern would occur if the pattern were extended. They confirmed their predictions by extending the pattern. They communicated their understanding of patterns by generalizing about the similarities and differences in the patterns they created. Finally, they used reasoning to determine why a sequence was not a pattern.

Answers

Page 48
Children create their own patterns with letters.

Page 49
1. A, AB
2. CCA
3. No
4. Yes
5. A
6. B
7. B

Name ____________________

Extending Patterns

Use the letters A and B to make a pattern.

______ ______ ______ ______ ______ ______ ______ ______

1. What is the 5th letter in the pattern? ____________

2. What is the 8th letter in the pattern? ____________

Use the letters A and B to make a different pattern.

______ ______ ______ ______ ______ ______ ______ ______

4. What is the 3rd letter in the pattern? ____________

5. What is the 5th letter in the pattern? ____________

Use the letters A and B to make a different pattern.

______ ______ ______ ______ ______ ______ ______ ______

6. What is the 3rd letter in the pattern? ____________

7. What is the 5th letter in the pattern? ____________

Name ______________________

Extending Patterns

Complete the patterns.

1. A B A B A B ___ B ___ ___

2. C C A C C A C C A ___ ___ ___

Is there a pattern? Circle the answer.

D E D F A

3. Yes or No

E H H E H H E H H

4. Yes or No

Use the pattern to answer the questions.

A B B A B B A B B

5. What will be the 10th letter in the pattern? ______________

6. What will be the 12th letter in the pattern? ______________

7. What will be the 15th letter in the pattern? ______________

Understanding Equality

Introduction

Objective → Children will begin to develop a conceptual understanding of equality. They will understand that the equal symbol means "is the same as."

Context → Children have used addition and subtraction sentences with numbers to 10. In future lessons, children will explore equality with subtraction.

f.y.i.

It is possible that the children have had experiences with pan balances, but not with number balances. If this is the case, give the children some time to explore with the number balance. If you are using pan balances, be sure each balance has 2 of each weight, 1 unit to 9 units.

NCTM Standards Focus

Children frequently approach the equal sign as a prompt to act on the numbers and symbols and supply an answer. They are usually not encouraged to broaden their understanding of equality until they are introduced to formal algebra in later grades. Through their exploration in this lesson, children are encouraged to understand the equal sign as a symbol that separates the two sides of an equation and states that the right side is the same as the left side.

Representation Children create and use concrete and written representations to express equality.

Communication Children communicate their ideas about equality to the class and try out each other's ideas on a balance.

Connections Children connect equality to their prior understanding of measure, number, and operations.

Teaching Plan

Materials → Student pages 54–55; number balances with math weights, or a balance scale with labeled weights of 1–9 grams or ounces; chart paper

SHOW THE BALANCE to the class. *What can you can tell me about the object you see here?* Have children make observations about the balance and tell what they know about it from previous experience. Be sure that at some point it is observed that the balance at rest is level.

Once children have made a variety of general comments about the balance, ask how it is used. *What do you think will happen if I place one of these weights on the 5 peg?* Encourage children to speculate on what might happen. Have a volunteer come forward and place the weight on the 5 peg.

DISCUSS WHAT IS HAPPENING and why. The discussion will focus on the weight of the object. *Is the balance level now? Where would you place a weight on the other side to make the balance level again?* Let children speculate where to place the second weight as a volunteer tries out their ideas. Keep going until the balance is level.

What happened to make the balance level? (Putting a 5 weight on both sides) You can say that 5 on this side is the same as 5 on the other side. Write the statement "5 is the same as 5" on the chart paper. Then write "5 = 5" as you explain that in math you show that 5 is the same as 5 this way. You say "five equals 5."

REMOVE THE WEIGHT from one side. *Can you think of a way to make the balance level again by using two weights on the empty side?* As children try different combinations, record each unsuccessful try on a new sheet of chart paper. For example, "2 and 6 is not the same as 5" or "2 + 6 is not the same as 5." When children come up with a combination that equals 5, record it on the original chart paper. For example, "5 is the same as 4 and 1, or 5 = 4 + 1."

Encourage children to find other combinations on the balance that equal 5. Record each successful combination on the chart of equalities. Once all the combinations for 5 are exhausted, take all the weights off the balance and start with a new number.

Distribute student page 54 and assign children partners or place them in groups, depending on how many balances you have. Go over the directions on the page and the pictures of balances with weights. Explain that children will discuss and try out each problem together. They will take turns with the balance so that everyone has a chance to use it. They should fill out their pages independently.

What Might Happen . . . What to Do

Some children might want to use only the same numbers on both sides of the balance. Play a "What If" game. Have children place a weight on each side of the balance to level it. Remove the weight from one side. *What if this peg gets broken? How can we make the balance level?* Help children see that they can use 2 numbers to equal the value of the lost number. Repeat this activity a few times.

f.y.i.

If the children are not clear on the meaning of the word *level*, show them with the balance. Then have them model the idea by holding their arms straight out from their bodies. Ask them to act out the balance being down on one side, then down on the other side, then level again.

CIRCULATE AMONG THE GROUPS as the children are working and have them tell you what they are doing. Be sure to ask questions about how to level the balance while stressing the idea of amounts that are equal, or "the same as."

Encourage children to record the equal amounts using the words *the same as* or *equal* or the equal sign. Some children may not be ready to use the symbolic representation; e.g., $3 + 5 = 1 + 7$. If they are more comfortable writing "3 and 5 is the same as 1 and 7," that's fine. Just be sure they write one kind of representation so they will have a visual image of an equation.

When children have completed the student page, have them discuss their results. While they are working and in the follow-up discussion, you might ask these questions:

- *What do you notice about the relationship between the numbers that you used to level your balance scale?*
- *Show me with your arms what the balance would look like if I put a weight of 7 on one side and a weight of 7 on the other side.*
- *What would the balance look like if one side were heavier than the other?*
- *What would the balance look like if one side were lighter than the other?*
- *How can you show this with numbers and words?*
- *How can you represent a level balance with numbers?*
- *How can you represent a level balance with words?*

What Might Happen . . . What to Do

As children work with the balances to complete student page 55, they might treat this as a guess, check, and revise activity. If children use this method, guide them to connect to their prior understanding of equal measurement and offer suggestions for how they should use what they know about the value of the numbers on each peg to determine where to place each weight.

Student Pages

Student page 54 provides pictures of balances for which children write the equations or draw on the weights. Student page 55 contains additional equalities for the children to complete.

Assessment

As children worked on the student pages, you could see whether they created equalities on the balance and represented those equalities in words or symbols. Through their work with the balances and their discussion, you noted whether or not children understood that different combinations can equal the same number, and then that two different combinations can equal each other.

NCTM Standards Summary

In this lesson, the children used balances to explore equality in a concrete way before they represented the idea with symbolic or verbal expressions. They expressed their ideas for creating equality and tried them out in the whole class and small groups. They connected this exploration to their prior knowledge of measuring weight as they used the balance, and to their prior knowledge of numbers and operations as they moved toward writing equations in symbolic terms.

Answers

Page 54

1. 6 is the same as 6, or $6 = 6$.
2. 3 and 2 is the same as 5, or $3 + 2 = 5$.
3. 9 is not the same as 3 and 4
4. 5 and 3 is not the same as 3 and 8.

Page 55

1. Weight added to 3 on the left; 4 and 3 is the same as 1 and 6, or $4 + 3 = 1 + 6$.
2. Weight added to 8 on the right; 7 and 3 is the same as 2 and 8, or $7 + 3 = 2 + 8$.
3. Weight added to 6 on the left; 4 and 6 is the same as 9 and 1, or $4 + 6 = 9 + 1$.
4. Weights added on the right to equal 5; possible answer: 3 and 2 is the same as 1 and 4.

Name ______________________

Understanding Equality

Use a balance. Match what the picture shows.
Write what the balance shows.

❶

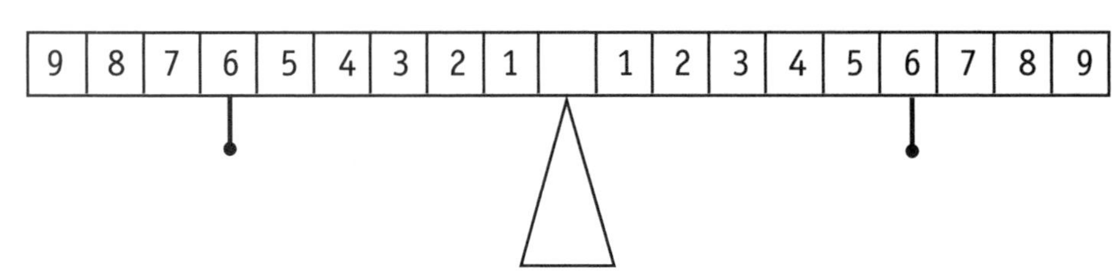

____

❷

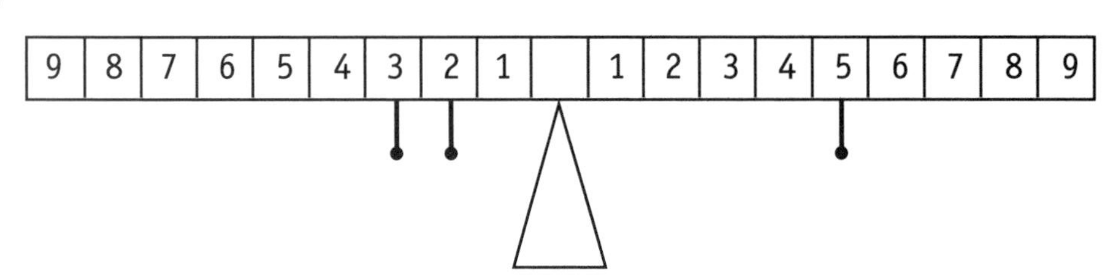

____

❸

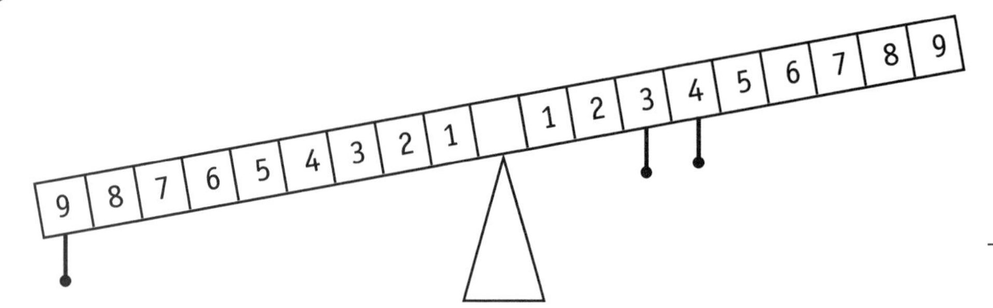

____

❹

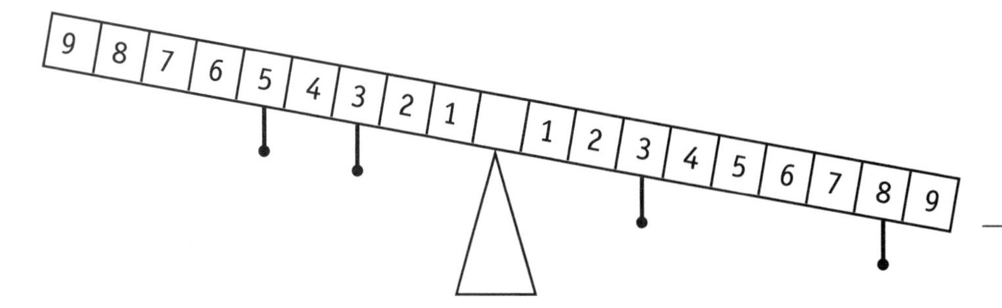

____

Name

Understanding Equality

Draw a weight on each balance to make it level.
Use a real balance to help. Write what the level balance shows.

❶
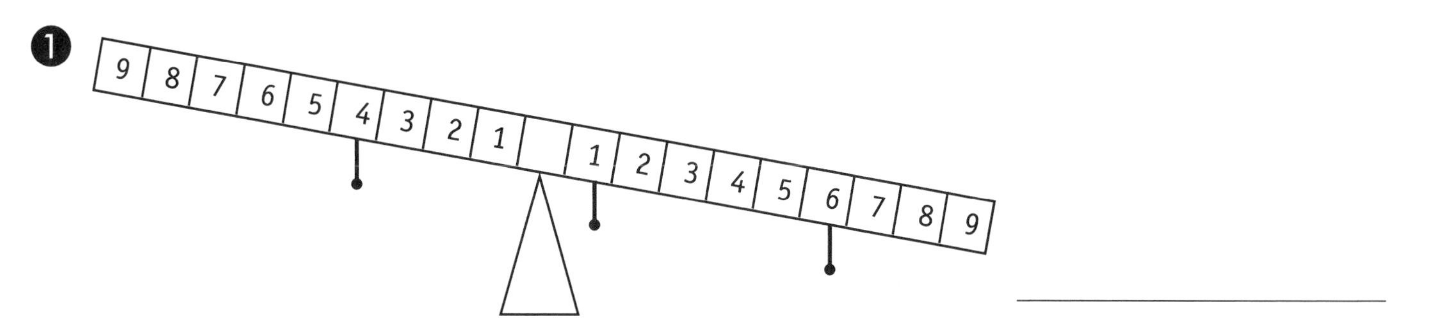

❷
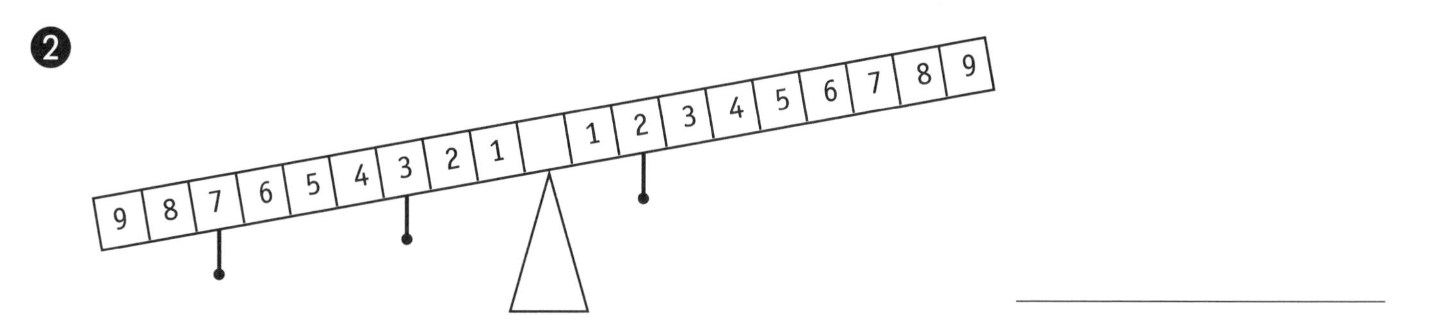

❸
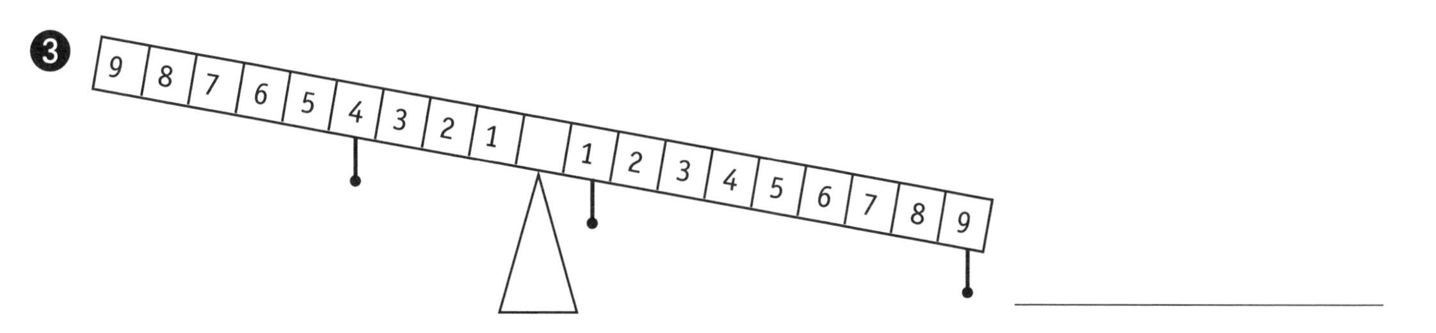

❹
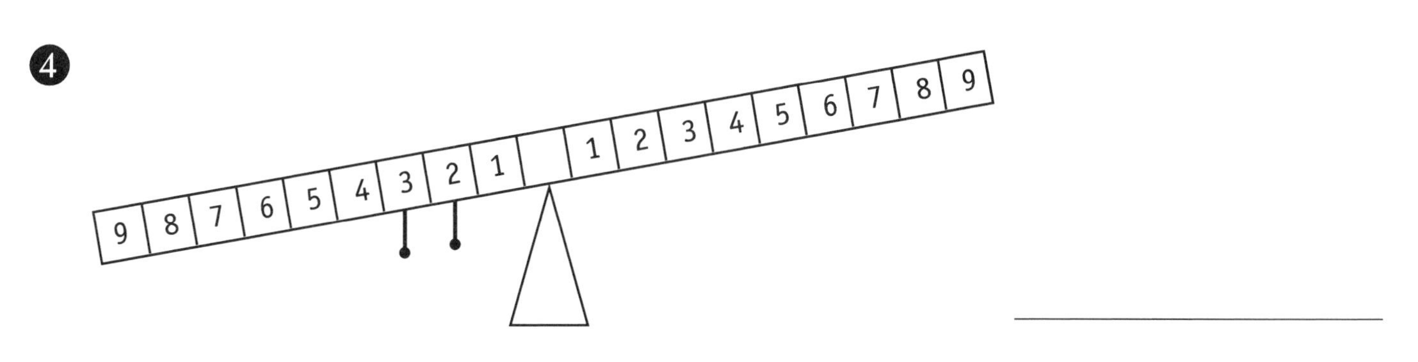

Representing Problems

Introduction

Objective → Children will use concrete, pictorial, and verbal representations of numerical situations, including invented notation, to represent and analyze mathematical situations and mathematical structures.

Context → Children have learned to count, add, and subtract. They will apply their knowledge of representing problem-solving situations to formal problem-solving strategies.

NCTM Standards Focus

The problem-solving situations in this lesson are challenging for children to solve since, rather than being simple *join* or *separate* problems, these can be solved using either addition or subtraction. Although there is only one correct answer for each problem, this standards-based lesson allows children to express their thinking and use different methods to find solutions.

Connections Children make connections between their understanding of addition and subtraction and representing problem situations.

Problem Solving Children devise their own methods for solving addition and subtraction problems.

Representation Children create and use representations to organize, record, and communicate mathematical ideas.

Teaching Plan

Materials → Student pages 60–61; concrete materials, such as cubes, counters, etc.; markers or crayons; chart paper

INTRODUCE THE FIRST STORY PROBLEM on student page 60 to the children. Read the problem aloud and take time to discuss what the problem is all about and what needs to be done to solve the problem. *Tell me something you know about this problem. What is it that we need to figure out? How many children are there in Sammi's class? Did his mom bake enough cookies for everyone? How do you know that 15 cookies are not enough?* Encourage children to bring out the variety of ways the problem situation can be represented.

Once children understand what they need to do to solve the problem, tell them that they may use counters or cubes to represent the problem. They should copy their representations by drawing pictures, writing words, or writing numbers, so that they can share their solutions with the class. Observe and listen to the methods they use. Have them describe what their representations show. Encourage them to express their thinking verbally.

As the children work to solve the problem, encourage them to describe the different methods they are using. Allow them to see that they can get the answer by either adding or subtracting.

Methods Children Might Use

- They might represent the total number of people that will be at the party using counters or cubes. They could show the number of cookies Sammi's mom has already baked and compare the two numbers by counting how many more people than cookies there are.
- They might count on from 15 to 24 and give the difference as their answer.
- They might use 24 counters to represent the total cookies that are needed. They could remove 15 and count what is left over.
- They might represent the solution using an addition or subtraction number sentence.

As children are sharing their methods, ask if anyone wrote a number sentence. If some children have written an addition sentence, ask if someone got the same answer by using a subtraction number sentence. As the methods and strategies are enumerated ask, *Did we all get the same answer to this problem even though we used different methods?* Help children see the value in using different methods to get the same answer.

Comparing or separating, although in and of themselves are two different concepts, are both shown symbolically as subtraction. Children can often see that separating one quantity from a total can be shown as subtraction, while comparison is not as clear a concept. Sometimes it is easier for children to deal with a comparison through addition. *How many more do you have to add so that both are the same?*

What Might Happen . . . What to Do

Some children might have reached a comfort level with one approach and may not be ready to try a new method. Encourage the children to teach each other the different methods they are using. This opportunity will help children learn about different methods and also focus on communicating their mathematical ideas.

Have children work in pairs or small groups to solve the other problems on the page. Encourage them to try a method that they have not used before and that was discussed while solving the first problem. They may also try a method that has not been discussed earlier.

Again, circulate among the groups. Listen to their discussions and ask questions about the methods they are using. If some children are solving the problems the same way as they did previously and are hesitant to try another method or strategy, have them complete the solution process they are involved in. Return to them later and ask them to tell you what they have done. Then guide them to think of another way to solve the problem.

After the children finish working, have them share their methods of representation; pictorial, concrete, verbal, or as a number sentence. When children use number sentences, take time to discuss how the number sentence relates to the representation they used to solve the problem.

To conclude the lesson, have children summarize the lesson by asking them to explain how they can solve problems in different ways and yet end up with the same answer.

Student Pages

Student page 60 provides problems for children to solve in pairs or in small groups. On student page 61, children solve additional problems using what they learned in the class discussion.

Assessment

Ongoing assessment occurred while children explained their thinking, described the methods or strategies they used, and represented their solution processes with a number sentence or a written account.

NCTM Standards Summary

Children connected their understanding of addition and subtraction to the representations they created in this lesson. They moved from a concrete representation to a visual representation to a symbolic representation. It was important to introduce different numerical situations and representations to children, so that they had many venues to explore and make sense of numbers and operations. Children used their procedural knowledge of operations as they developed a conceptual knowledge of the operations and made sense of problem situations.

Answers

Page 60

1. 9 cookies
2. 15 cupcakes
3. 25 books

Page 61

1. 4 blocks
2. 12th floor
3. 2 cats and dogs or 1 cat and 1 dog

Name

Representing Problems

Use counters or cubes to solve. Draw pictures of what you did. Use numbers or words to tell how you solved the problems.

1. Sammi's mom is baking jumbo cookies for his party. So far she has baked 15 cookies. There will be 24 children at the party. Everyone needs to get a cookie.

   How many more cookies does Sammi's mom need to bake?

2. Andy's dad baked 30 cupcakes for the party. He needs only 15 cupcakes for the party. How many cupcakes are left over?

3. Milan has 19 books. Keesha has 6 more books than Milan. How many books does Keesha have?

Name

Representing Problems

Use counters or cubes to solve. Draw pictures of what you did. Use numbers or words to tell how you solved the problems.

1. Stella makes a pattern with 7 blocks. Ronnie's pattern has 11 blocks. How many more blocks does Ronnie's pattern have?

2. Allie and Frank are friends and live in the same building. Allie takes the elevator down 7 floors to Frank's floor. They then take the elevator together 5 more floors down to the first floor. On what floor does Allie live?

3. Marc has 5 pets. He has 3 more fish than cats and dogs. How many cats and dogs does he have?

Choosing the Operation

Introduction

Objective → Children will solve addition and subtraction problems by choosing the operation.

Context → This lesson comes towards the end of a unit on addition and subtraction. Children have practiced adding to and subtracting from numbers up to 12. Future lessons may include problem-solving activites with calculators.

Name ____________

Choosing the Operation

Learn

Write + or − in the □. Add or subtract.

Paul has 7 pencils. He gives 3 to his sister. How many pencils does he have left?

7
[−]3
4

Try

Lisa has 3 blocks. Her mother gives her 2 more. How many blocks does she have?

3
□2
___

Practice

1. There are 5 books on the table. There are 3 more on the chair. How many books are there in all?

5
□3
___

NCTM Process Standards Analysis and Focus

The standards analysis examines how the process standards have been incorporated into the above lesson. By increasing the focus on three of the process standards, a more effective and meaningful lesson can be presented. The suggestions offered can help you to think about how this might be accomplished.

Problem Solving Several story problems are presented, but no investigation is called for in the lesson. Children simply complete problems by filling in an operational sign and an answer.

Suggestion → **Have children create their own addition and/or subtraction problems. Constructing and describing mathematical situations will strengthen children's understanding of operations.**

Name ______________________

2. Steve has 6 blue marbles and 3 yellow marbles. How many marbles does he have in all?

6
☐3
___

___

3. Ariel has 11 balloons. 7 balloons are red. The other balloons are green. How many green balloons does Ariel have?

11
☐7
___

___

4. Meagan has 9 marbles. 4 marbles roll away. How many does she have left?

9
☐4
___

___

5. Anna has 4 crayons and Keith has 4 crayons. How many crayons do they have in all?

4
☐4
___

___

Communication Rather than being engaged in discussion, children are asked simple questions that require them to repeat information found in the examples on the page.

Suggestion → **Provide opportunities for children to share the problems they have created with the class and in small groups. This will promote discussion about the rationale for each operation, which will, in turn, promote further understanding of addition and subtraction. As children discuss various mathematical situations, they also practice using appropriate mathematical language.**

Representation The lesson uses pictures to represent the first number described in each story problem.

Suggestion → **Have children represent each story problem with manipulatives and/or drawings. These models will help children visualize whether items are being combined (addition) or removed (subtraction). Challenge children to use symbols to represent related mathematical situations for addition. This will facilitate abstract thinking.**

Reasoning and Proof Children are not asked to explain their thinking or to check their answers.

Connections Connections to mathematical thinking are not made.

The teaching plan that follows shows how the suggestions for increasing the focus on the process standards can be implemented.

Revised Teaching Plan

Materials → Manipulatives such as counters and cubes; chart paper; construction paper; markers; tape recorder

ASK CHILDREN TO LISTEN AS YOU PRESENT three or four story problems. After each one, ask children to generate questions that get at the operation required to solve the problem. Start with stories A, B, and C below, and then continue by making up your own. Vary the situations to challenge children to consider both addition and subtraction. Also include a situation that does not call for an operation, such as *There were 6 grasshoppers and 4 crickets. Were there more crickets or grasshoppers?* Presenting this type of situation focuses thinking on the information needed to determine whether addition or subtraction is called for.

As you present each story situation, allow time for children to think about the information and then generate questions. Record children's questions on the board or on chart paper. Then revisit the chart to determine and write a number sentence for each situation. Provide time for children to share their thinking. *How do you know what to do to solve the problem? What details or words help you to know?* Encouraging children to generate their own questions offers a meaningful context to investigate mathematical ideas. Children become actively involved in using information to think about what is happening in each situation to determine if combining or separating is taking place.

Story A

There were 7 robins and 5 cardinals.

What are some questions we could ask about the number of birds in the story? Facilitate discussion to help children generate questions such as:

- *How many birds were there altogether?*
- *Were there more robins than cardinals? How many more robins than cardinals were there?*
- *Were there fewer cardinals than robins? How many fewer?*

Story B

8 cows were in the pasture. 5 went to the pond to get a drink.

How many cows were still in the pasture?

f.y.i.

Story B presents a subtraction situation in which a part is removed from the whole, whereas Story C offers a chance to use the comparison model of subtraction. It is important for children to be aware of different subtraction models.

What Might Happen . . . What to Do

Children may have difficulty generating questions for the described situation. Have children describe what happened in this story. Children should be able to give a general description telling that there were cows in the pasture and some left. *Do we know how many cows there were at the beginning? Do we know how many cows left to go to the pond? How can we find out how many cows stayed?* Modeling with manipulatives or drawing a picture to represent what happened will reinforce how many items are being taken away. Link subtraction to the concept of removing. Then ask children to help you write a number sentence to represent what happened.

Story C

There were 4 plain butterflies by the roses. There were 5 butterflies with spots by the lilies.

Children might come up with questions such as:

- *How many butterflies were there altogether?*
- *How many more butterflies are spotted than plain?*
- *How many fewer butterflies are plain than spotted?*

ORGANIZE CHILDREN INTO SMALL GROUPS of 3 to 5. Provide each group with two or three stories similar to the examples above. If possible, record the information on a tape recorder or provide activity cards for group members to use as a reference. Distribute sheets of construction paper, markers, and manipulatives to each group. Have children represent what happens in each problem by using the manipulatives or by drawing pictures. Then children can write one question for each situation on the construction paper. Challenge each group to write the number sentence that describes their question. Using a range of models to represent each situation helps children to better visualize the process as well as determine the answer.

Allow time for groups to share their questions and number sentences. As groups present their number stories, encourage classmates to listen carefully and ask questions or add insights. Invite groups to share different strategies for the same situation.

Ask children to explain their thinking as they describe their decision-making process. *How did you find your answer? Can you show us what you did either by using manipulatives or by explaining your drawing? Did you combine (put together) or separate (take apart or remove)? How did you know whether you needed to put together or take away? How did you describe the situation with a number sentence?*

REPEAT THIS PROCEDURE FOR EACH SITUATION PRESENTED. Planning both small- and large-group discussions gives different contexts for children to express their findings. Discussing ideas allows children to experience the importance of questioning each other's strategies and results in helping them clarify their own understandings. These exchanges also give children a chance to see and value a range of solutions to various problems.

Display children's questions and drawings in the math center and make manipulatives available. As children visit the center, encourage them to use manipulatives to act out their classmates' story situations.

Student Pages

Children are now ready to complete excercises similar to those on the reduced student pages.

Assessment

As children created their own story problems, it was possible to observe and assess how they determined which operation to use to solve each problem. Their ability to connect the correct operation with the problem could easily be assessed as they wrote number sentences to represent each mathematical situation.

NCTM Standards Summary

Throughout the lesson, children had repeated opportunities to think about situations and select which operation, addition or subtraction, described them. Allowing children to generate their own questions enhanced the level of their engagement with the activity. As children discussed details and relationships with classmates, they analyzed whether situations represented items being combined for addition or those being removed for subtraction. The small-group and whole-class discussions provided time for children to reflect and express their mathematical understandings. In addition, children used various models, such as manipulatives, drawings, and number sentences, to represent mathematical situations. This broad range of representations enhanced children's ability to visualize the underlying rationale for each of the operations.

Standard 3 **Geometry**

AT THE FIRST GRADE LEVEL, geometry includes a lot of work with solid and plane shapes, developing mental images of shapes, and describing movements. Our lessons are derived from these important topics, and include a lesson on creating mental images, a lesson on describing movements, a lesson that explores different shapes, and a lesson that includes solid and plane shapes.

Three lessons model how the process standards can be used to teach content. A fourth lesson is a hypothetical textbook lesson that we have revised to be more standards based. These four lessons do not represent the entire curriculum, but rather provide glimpses of how, with a more concentrated effort to incorporate the process standards, better mathematics teaching and learning can be achieved.

One lesson we have chosen is a lesson that tries to develop mental images of shapes in children's minds. Through the process standards of representation, communication, and reasoning and proof, children use physical objects to represent a visual image. By discussing their thinking and describing their objects, children are able to develop accurate images.

Another lesson we have chosen is a lesson that focuses children on being able to describe movements using direction and distance. Rather than just learning the words, children physically perform the movements. This allows them to make stronger connections with the vocabulary. Children are also asked to write their own directions.

A third lesson we have chosen is a lesson in which children explore two new shapes, the parallelogram and the trapezoid. By incorporating a problem-solving approach, children use triangles to form these new shapes. They communicate how they know what each shape is that they form.

The hypothetical textbook lesson we have chosen to revise is a lesson that has children matching geometric solids with drawings of their faces. Through better incorporation of the process standards of reasoning and proof, communication, and connections, children will see how geometric forms are used in their environment. Allowing children time to discuss the attributes and compare many objects will help their thinking about the shapes.

Standard 3 Lessons

Creating Mental Images

Introduction

Objective → Children will build and manipulate mental representations of shapes, relationships, and transformations.

Context → Children have used and described the positions of different geometric shapes. They are familiar with making patterns and describing the repeating part of the pattern or pattern rule. They will continue to apply and describe movements using directional language.

NCTM Standards Focus

The ability to visualize, especially shapes and patterns, is an important skill in math. Young children need to create a mental picture and to represent it physically. They then create the pictorial level for themselves. In this hands-on activity, children manipulate shapes physically until their memory of the images and their representations align. They then represent and complete the activity pictorially.

Representation Children use physical objects to represent a visual image. The page they use helps them organize and record the activity using the following steps: image → physical representation → pictorial representation.

Communication As they work in groups, children communicate the strategies they use to represent the position of shapes. They listen to, and question, methods and conclusions that they are introduced to.

Reasoning and Proof Children use reasoning skills in developing strategies for placing their blocks and for determining whether they have placed them in the correct position.

Teaching Plan

Materials → Student pages 74–75; handful of a selection of all pattern blocks; overhead projector; overhead pattern blocks; transparency of student page 74 (you may wish to make several copies per child); crayons

GIVE CHILDREN PATTERN BLOCKS and student page 74. Have them turn the page over and use it as a mat for exploring with the pattern blocks for several minutes. While they are doing this, walk around the class and ask children to describe the different shapes. Encourage them to use as many different descriptions as possible. *What else can you tell about the yellow shape? How many sides does the yellow hexagon have? When you compare the hexagon to the red shape, is it bigger or smaller?*

ASK THE CHILDREN to clear their mats after they have had time to explore with the shapes. Have them turn the student page over so that the four quadrants are visible. Use the transparency of the same student page and place it on the overhead projector. *I am going to place a pattern block on this sheet. After you have had a chance to see where I put the block, I'm going to take it away. I want you to choose the same pattern block and place it in the same place on your sheet.* Place a hexagon in the top right quadrant so that one vertex touches the vertical axis and one side is on the horizontal axis. Give children about 5–10 seconds to look at the block and note its placement before turning the overhead off.

Your goal in this part of the activity is to have children create a visual image, then a concrete representation of that image, and then a pictorial image.

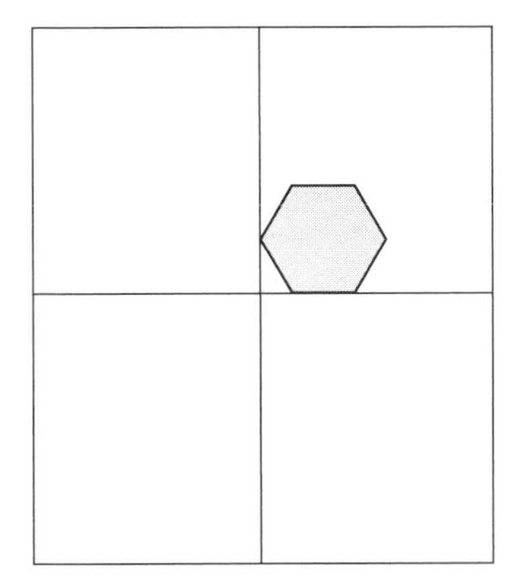

f.y.i.

If you do not have a sufficient number of pattern blocks, you can use construction paper cut-outs of pattern blocks. As you duplicate the shapes, duplicate the colors as well.

CIRCULATE AMONG THE CHILDREN to see what they have done. Discuss with children what they were thinking as they chose the shape and placed it on their grids. *How did you remember which shape to use? How did you remember where to place the shape? How did you remember what part of the grid to place the shape in? Did anyone use any different strategies to remember which shape to use and where to place this block?*

f.y.i.

If children have used construction paper cut-outs of pattern blocks, you might want to have them paste these shapes onto the quadrant rather than have them trace and color the shape in place.

Next, turn the overhead back on and have children verify that they are using the correct shape and have placed it correctly. Allow time for children to make corrections as needed. Then ask children to trace the hexagon and color it.

The answers the children give will provide you with clues about how to continue the discussion. Most of the questions above focus on what is important for children to notice about the block and its placement, and then how to represent their mental images on the page in front of them. Encourage them to tell how they first looked at the shape that you placed on the overhead. Ask them to describe what they said to themselves as they chose the shape and placed it on the student page. Have them tell what it was that they paid attention to besides the color of the shape.

Continue the lesson by placing the yellow hexagon in different positions and in different quadrants on the overhead. Each time have children represent the block and its placement on their pages. Have them trace the hexagon and color it. Go through the same discussion points as with the first placement.

What Might Happen . . . What to Do

Depending on the children's experiences, they might find choosing the correct shape confusing. Spend some time with children describing the shapes. After a while they should begin to pay attention to other attributes besides color, such as size and the number of sides. Encourage children to learn the names of the shapes by repeating the name of the shape after each attribute: for example, the blue rhombus, the red trapezoid, and the yellow hexagon.

Discuss with the children how they placed their shapes and how they corrected their placement if needed. This encourages them to compare two placements at a distance from each other. They are going to have to make a one-to-one comparison first: e.g. shape to shape, quadrant to quadrant, etc. As they become accustomed to the activity, they will be able to create mental images in their comparisons incorporating more than one attribute. This will then enhance their ability to replicate new placements.

Reinforce mathematical vocabulary of description, placement, name, or direction such as, left, right, above, below, top, bottom, long side, short side, parallelogram, rhombus, triangle, hexagon, square, and trapezoid.

Questioning the children while they are doing the activity is of utmost importance. These questions should relate to the idea of shape and placement. *Which shape are you using? How do you know? Where is the shape on the paper?* This forces the children to pay attention to how they remember or visualize things.

Student Pages

Student page 74 provides children with the four quadrants needed to anchor the placements of the shape to the page. Student page 75 can be used for a center activity or be sent home for children to do with a family member. Children place cutout shapes according to given directions.

Assessment

As you observed the children replicate the placement of the hexagon, you had an opportunity to evaluate their strategies for remembering the shape and where it was placed in one plane and transferring it to another plane. You were also able to assess how well they communicated strategies and methods for carrying out the activity.

NCTM Standards Summary

Children represented visual images using physical pattern blocks by duplicating placement and orientation of the shapes on student page 74. They communicated their thoughts and methods as they shared their thinking with you and their classmates. They communicated placement using directional, positional, and mathematical vocabulary. They represented the physical placement by tracing the shape in the correct position.

Answers

Page 74
Answers may vary.

Page 75
Children place shapes according to the directions given.

Name

Creating Mental Images

Trace and color the shape.

Name

Creating Mental Images

Cut out the shapes. Place them in the correct box.
Color the shapes.

Place the in the middle inside this space.

Place the on the left side inside this space.

Place the on the bottom inside this space.

Place the on the right side inside this space.

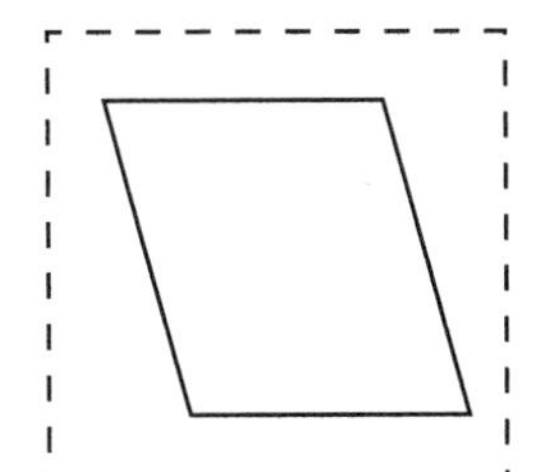
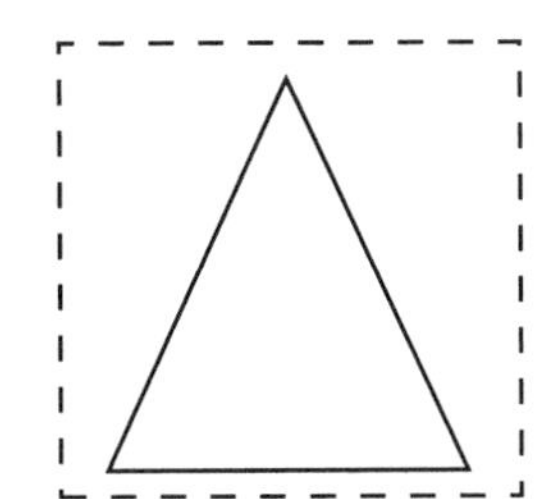
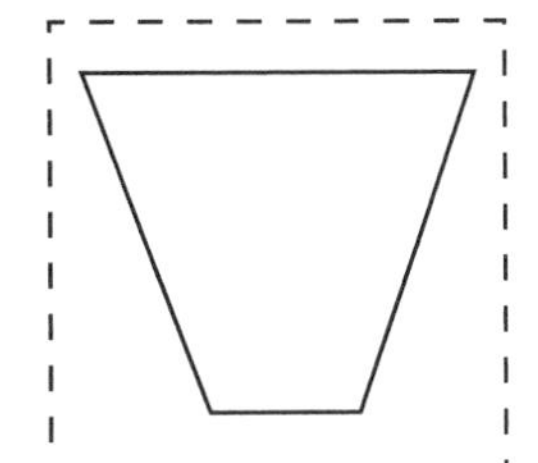
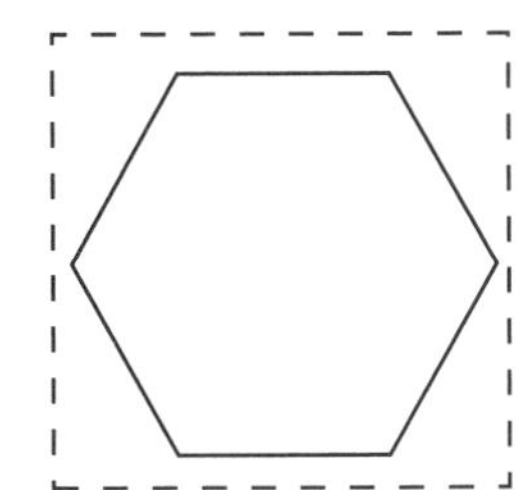

Describing Movements

Introduction

Objective → Children will interpret and apply ideas of direction and distance in navigating space.

Context → Children have used directional language as they have placed geometric shapes according to directions. They will continue following and applying directions as they move from geometry to data.

NCTM Standards Focus

Most of the children's experiences with directions are abstract—done with paper and pencil. In this standards-based lesson, children have an opportunity to follow directions using kinesthetic experiences before they process directions abstractly. This lesson allows children to make their own physical-to-abstract connections.

Connections Children make connections between kinesthetic and verbal understanding of directions. They also connect visual directions to actual movements.

Communication Children listen to directions and follow them. They write their own directions or clues.

Representation Children represent the directions with actual movements, drawings and symbols.

Teaching Plan

Materials → Student pages 80–81; masking tape; crayons

THE LESSON BEGINS WITH A REVIEW of direction. Then children will apply these concepts in a game of Teacher Says, a variation of Simon Says. Finally the children will complete student pages in which they follow and write their own direction clues.

To get children ready to play the game, review the concepts of *right, left, forward* and *backward*. Have the children gather on the floor in a common meeting area. *What does it mean if I say "turn to the right"?* Have some volunteers act out the direction. *How did you know in which direction to turn?* Do the same review for left, backward and forward. Have the children move one or more steps when you give a direction. *Show me 3 steps to the right. Now try 3 steps forward. Show me 5 steps backward. Show me what it means to move 4 steps to the left.*

Tell children that these directions can be represented by written symbols. Draw a direction arrow (→) for *right* on the board. Ask a volunteer to make the corresponding move. Do the same for left (←), backward (↓) and forward (↑). Have children practice the directions by moving in response to arrows that you write on the board. Then add a number to the arrow to indicate the number of steps. Have children practice this, making sure that all of them understand that they need to know both direction and the number of steps. Reverse the thinking by giving them the direction verbally, asking a child to act it out, and then having another child draw the appropriate arrow on the board.

f.y.i.

Write the words *right, left, forward,* and *backward* and draw the arrows on the board or a sheet of chart paper. You might want to establish a Math Word Wall and include these words on it. The words should be easily accessible to the children.

HAVE CHILDREN RETURN TO THEIR DESKS. Tell them they are going to play a game called "Teacher Says." To play "Teacher Says" mark a starting point on the floor with masking tape. Have a volunteer stand on the starting mark. Tell the class that you are thinking of an object in the room. Explain that you are going to give specific directions to the volunteer. If the child listens carefully and follows the directions exactly, he will arrive at the object you are thinking of. For example, you might say, *Teacher says take 3 steps forward.* Then the child would take 3 steps forward and stop. You give another direction, the child responds again, and so on until the child reaches the goal. There are two rules: 1) The child has to make the correct response to your directions. 2) If you do not say, "Teacher says," but just give the direction, and the child moves—that child is out and another child takes his or her place.

f.y.i.

You might wish to mark your starting point on the floor and pace out the distances before class. Depending upon the ability of the class, you may wish to have children take over your role. Challenge them to think of an object and then direct another child to it.

Have the class help the child decide which way to move after each clue. It is recommended that a child be able to reach the goal within three or four commands from the teacher. After several rounds, challenge children with a final round in which they move in response to an arrow clue you have drawn on the board. As you are doing the activity, ask children to share how they remember which direction is *left* and which is *right*. When giving directions to a child, you might want to reiterate some of the directions or ask the volunteer to do so. *How many steps do you need to move? Are you moving forward or backward? Which is right and which is left?*

What Might Happen . . . What to Do

Some children might have difficulties following directions or distinguishing between right and left. You might want to have these children play "Teachers Says" with a partner. If the children find distinguishing between right and left difficult, stamp their right hands. Ask them to refer to their hands to help them decide which way to turn.

Distribute student pages 80 and 81. Ask children to get out their crayons. Review with children how to complete the pages. Tell children that they will be using both pages to go on an imaginary treasure hunt. On page 80, they will be using the directional clues at the bottom of the page to follow the path to the treasure. This is an important activity because it helps children internalize the directions: right, left, forward, and backward. The activity also helps children make connections between the directions as they experienced them physically and as they are expressed on paper. After children complete page 80, invite them to discuss what they did. *How was the treasure hunt similar to what we did in class? How is moving forward or backward on paper different from physically moving forward or backward?*

Tell children that on page 81 they will be choosing their own paths to the treasure and listing the direction clues for getting there. This activity, like the previous one, is a sort of Logo® on paper. It, too, gives children opportunities to make connections between physical movement and its representation on paper. You might want to let children work in twos or small groups. Page 81 can be taken home to be completed.

Student Pages

On student page 80, children follow direction clues to draw a path from the black starting square to the treasure square. Student page 81 can be done at home or in class. The children create their own path to the treasure and record the correct directional clues.

Assessment

During the class activity you determined which children know right, left, forward, and backward depending on how they followed the directions in the physical activity as well as on the student page. You were also able to see how well the children could follow oral directions by where they ended up, either physically or on the page.

NCTM Standards Summary

Children connected previous knowledge of direction to the physical activity of listening and following verbal commands. They distinguished between directional words as they moved physically from one place to another. They connected the experience of movement to communication by writing their own directions.

Answers

Page 80
Path will follow directions.

Page 81
Answers may vary.

Name

Describing Movements

Use the arrow directions to get to the treasure.
Color the path that you make.

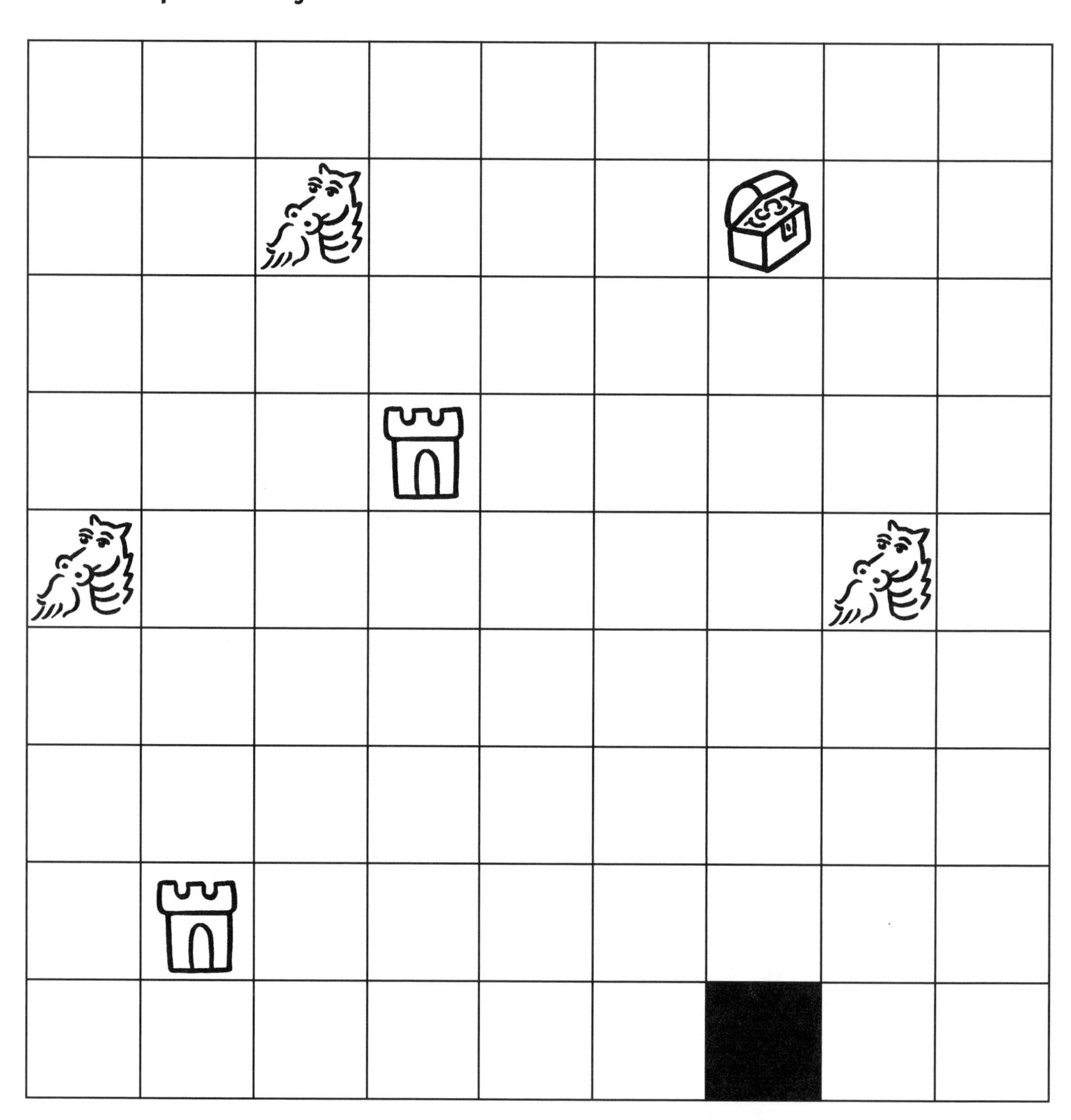

Start at ■. Go 4 ↑, 5 ←, 4 ↑, 5 →, 1 ↓

Name ______________________________

Describing Movements

How can you move from the woods to the castle?
Write the clues.

____

____

____

____

Exploring Shapes

Introduction

Objective → Children will describe various polygons. They will use congruent triangles to create the figures they describe.

Context → Children have been introduced to triangles, squares, and rectangles. In this lesson they will focus on the characteristics of those shapes and learn two new shapes, the parallelogram and the trapezoid. Later children will study three-dimensional shapes.

NCTM Standards Focus

In this lesson the children use problem-solving techniques as they form triangles, squares, rectangles, parallelograms, and trapezoids from congruent isosceles right triangles. This activity will help children develop a visual image of the attributes of the different shapes. As children manipulate the shapes, they reinforce their understanding of the attributes of each shape. Sharing descriptions of the shapes and how they made them gives children opportunities to develop more of the vocabulary of geometry. Children also compare different representations of a shape to verify that the shapes are the same.

Problem Solving The children apply problem-solving strategies as they devise their own methods for making different geometric shapes with triangles.

Representation Children use triangles to represent different shapes. They determine whether or not these representations match other representations of the shapes.

Communication Children describe the shapes and their attributes and explain to each other how they made the shapes. Class discussion gives children opportunities to build the vocabulary of geometry.

Teaching Plan

Materials → Student pages 86–87; scissors; tape and/or large white paper

TELL THE CHILDREN THAT TODAY they are going to make shapes using other shapes. Give each child a copy of student page 86. Ask the children about the figure on that page. *What is the figure?* (A square) *How do you know?* (Sides are the same length.) *What else do you notice about the shape?* Encourage children to talk about the square and the two diagonal lines that form the four triangles inside the square. If no one volunteers the terminology "diagonal lines," rephrase the children's observations about the square and the triangles to introduce "diagonal lines."

Have children color over the diagonals with a crayon. Then have them cut out the square and then cut it into four triangles. Encourage children to cut in the middle of the colored lines outlining the triangles, so that each triangle retains some of the outlining.

Ask children what other shapes besides the square they think they can make with one, two, three or all of the four triangles that they have. Allow them some time to freely explore joining the pieces together to form shapes. Tell them that after they have had some time to explore, you will ask them to try to make some particular shapes.

AFTER CHILDREN HAVE HAD about five minutes of free exploration call them back together and give each of them a copy of student page 87. This page shows examples of the following figures: a triangle, a square, a non-square rectangle, a parallelogram, and a trapezoid. The figures on this page are smaller versions of the figures that children will be making with the triangle. Discuss the shapes with the children. Ask them what they think is special about each figure. Encourage them to use the vocabulary of geometry as appropriate. Introduce the names of the figures even though children at this level are not required to use them. Ask children to compare the figures to each other and tell what is the same and what is different.

What Children Might Say

- All the figures but the triangle have the same number of sides.
- The square and the rectangle have angles, or corners, that are the same.
- The parallelogram has sides like the rectangle but its angles are different. It is "slanted" or "tipped."
- The trapezoid is like the rectangle but the top side is shorter. This makes the angles different.

Now tell children that they are to try to make each one of the shapes using their triangles. They can use one, two, three, or four triangles to make a shape. After they make the shape they should record it. They can tape the triangles together, or you can have children sketch or trace what they did on a piece of chart paper. Have them check off each figure after they make it.

WHILE CHILDREN ARE WORKING, circulate among them. Ask them what shapes they are making and what strategies they are using. *Can you make the same shape with a different number of triangles?* (For example, a triangle can be made with one, two, or four triangles.) Encourage children to try to make the same shape using different numbers of triangles.

Have the children name the shapes that they are making. Ask them to explain how they manipulated the pieces to produce the shape. *Do you think*

f.y.i.

You might want to reproduce student page 86 on heavier paper to make it easier for the children to manipulate the triangles. If you use heavier materials, you might want to pre-cut the materials and show children your page 86 for discussion. You might also want to give children several sets of triangles so that they can tape the triangles together as they form the shapes on student page 87.

f.y.i.

Enter the names of the shapes on chart paper. Draw a small picture of each shape next to its name. Make sure that the shapes are shown as irregular as well as regular shapes.

you will be able to put all four pieces together to make a rectangle that is longer on two sides than on the other two sides? How do you know?

When children have made a shape, ask them how they know it is the correct shape. Encourage them to use as many different descriptions as possible to convince you that the shape they have formed is similar to the one on the student page.

What Might Happen . . . What to Do

Some children might find it difficult to arrange the triangles into other geometric shapes. Work with these children individually or in a small group. Encourage them to first place two triangles in different ways. Discuss with them what the various combinations look like. You might need to show them how turning or rotating the pieces will give different shapes. Do this slowly and discuss each shape, how it was formed, what it looks like.

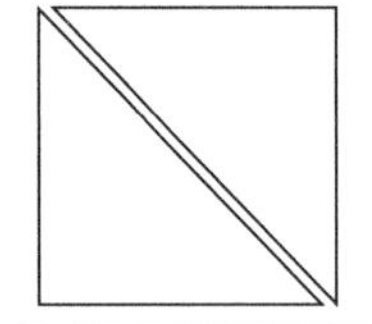

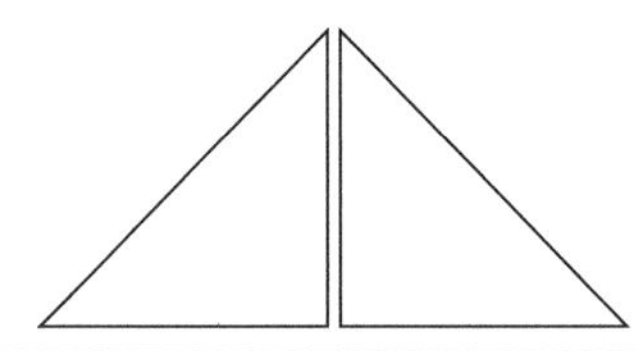

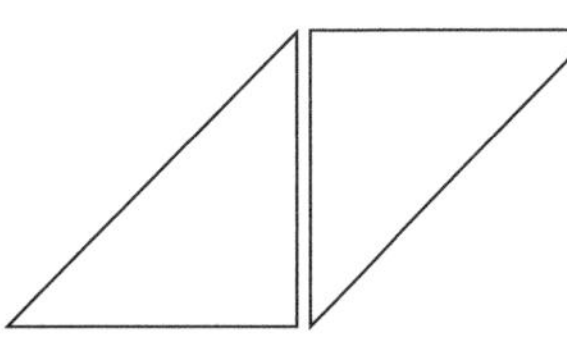

After children have had enough time to make most of the shapes, gather them together with their tracings or taped-together shapes. Discuss how they represented the different shapes they made. Make sure they explain how they know their shapes are similar to the shapes on student page 87. *What shapes were you able to make? What shapes could you not represent with these triangles?* If a child says that a particular shape could not be formed, ask if any one else formed that shape. If someone did, have him or her show the shape. If no one believes the shape can be made, lead children through the first step or two of making the shape and encourage them to continue from there.

Extension

Have children work in pairs and use two sets of triangles. *Can you make more shapes with two sets of triangles? What are they? Are there shapes you could not make with one set? Why not?* Work together to name the shapes that they made.

Student Pages

Student page 86 contains the square with diagonal lines forming 4 isosceles right triangles. Children cut out the figure and use the triangles to form other geometric shapes. Student page 87 contains five geometric shapes that children are to make. Both pages are used during the lesson.

Assessment

As you observed children work on the activity, you were able to evaluate their visual reasoning and perception, their knowledge of the shapes, and the problem-solving strategies they used. You saw which shapes were easier for children to form and which ones were more difficult. You assessed the children's spatial sense as they completed the task. As they communicated their methods and strategies for completing the shapes, you were able to evaluate their knowledge of geometric and mathematical language.

NCTM Standards Summary

The children discussed characteristics of various polygons. They represented different shapes with congruent isosceles right-angled triangles. They used problem-solving and spatial visualization strategies to make the shapes, and they communicated how their polygons reflected the properties of the shapes on the student page.

Answers

Page 86
There are no answers.

Page 87
Answers may vary. All the shapes can be made.

Name

Exploring Shapes

Cut along the black lines.

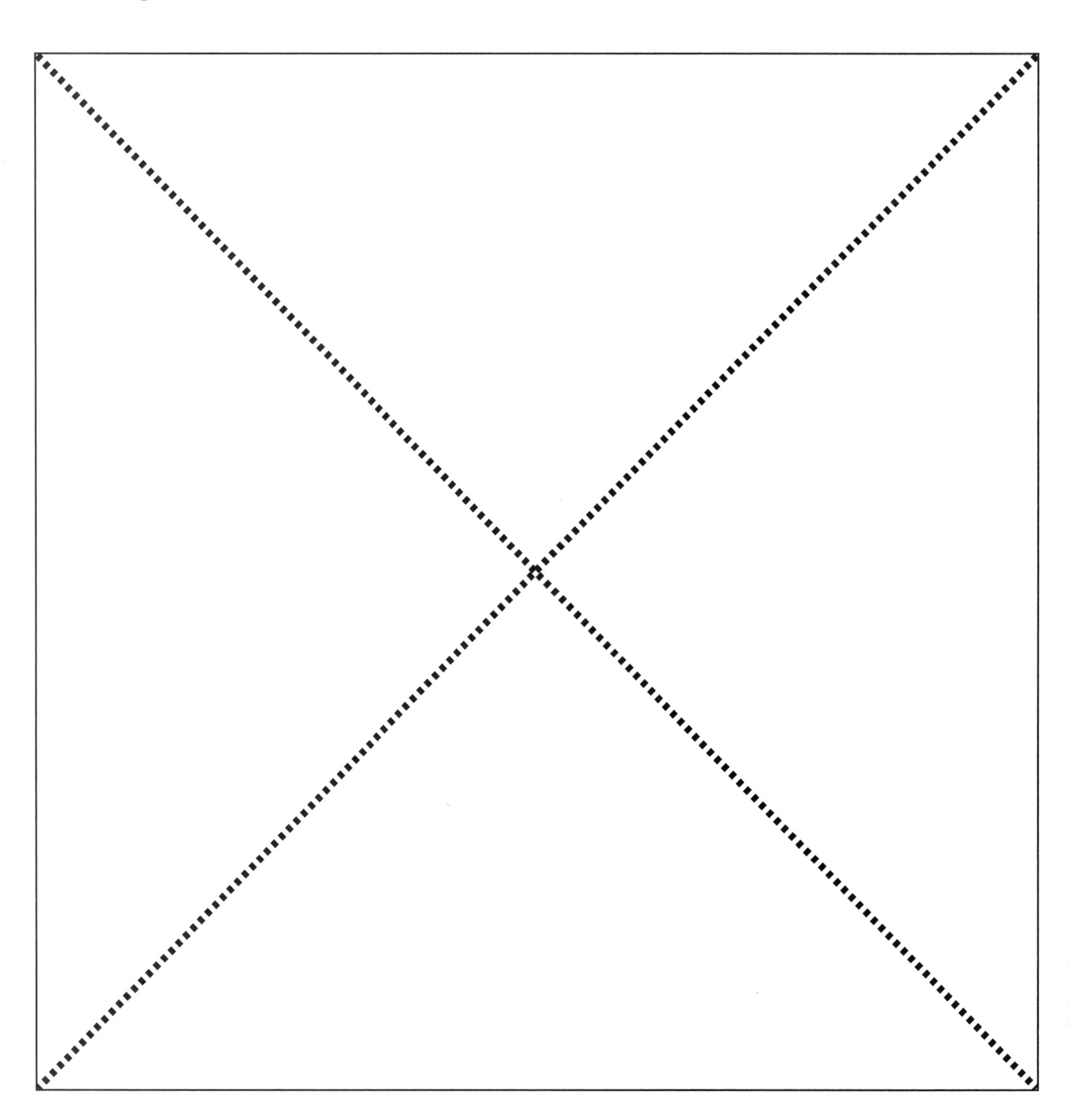

Name

Exploring Shapes

Use your triangles. Make each shape.

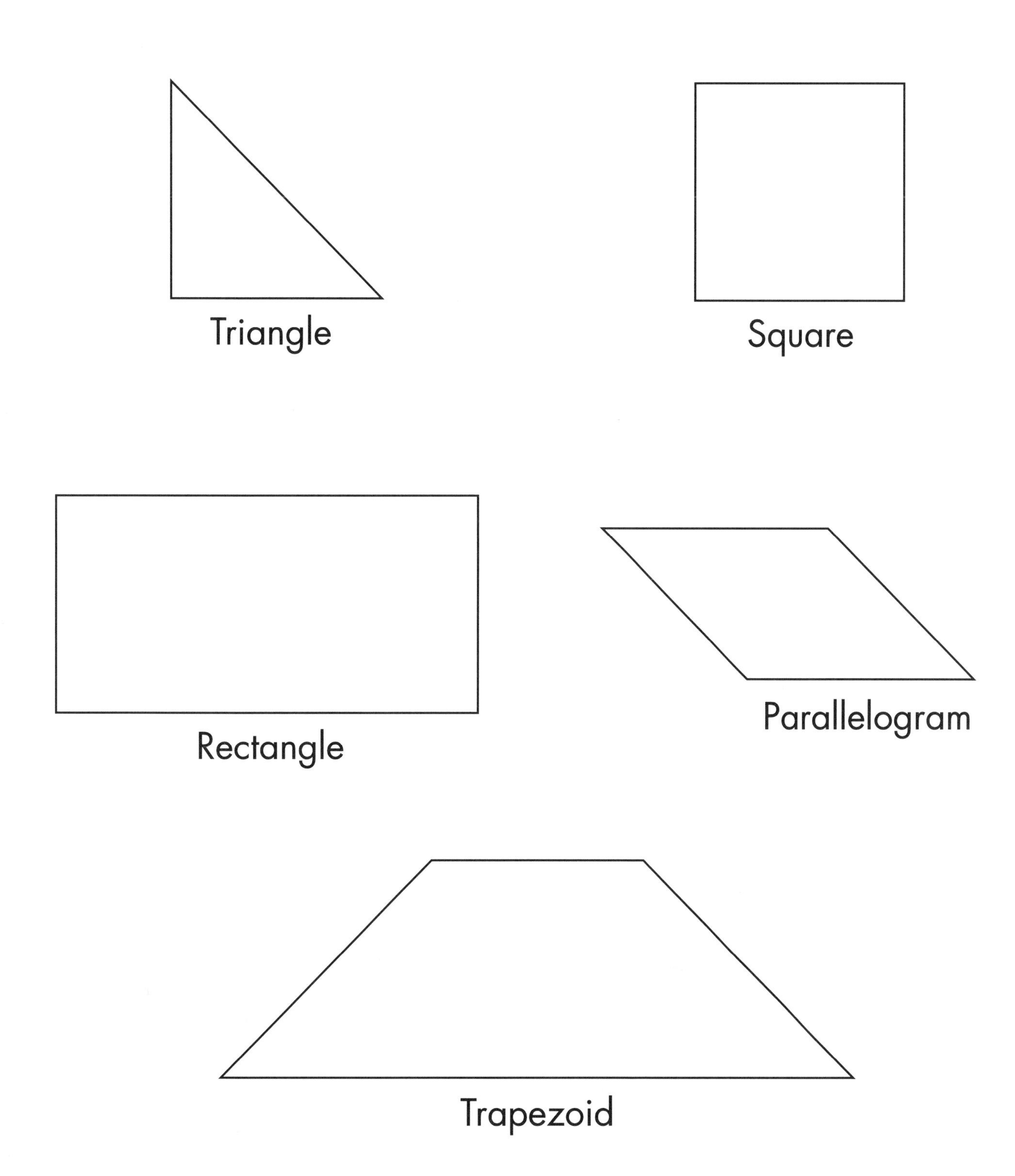

Investigating Solid and Plane Shapes

Introduction

Objective → Children will match geometric solids with drawings of faces found on those solids.

Context → This lesson takes place towards the beginning of a unit on geometry. Children have identified geometric solids such as cones, spheres, cubes, and cylinders. Subsequent lessons will focus on attributes of two-dimensional shapes.

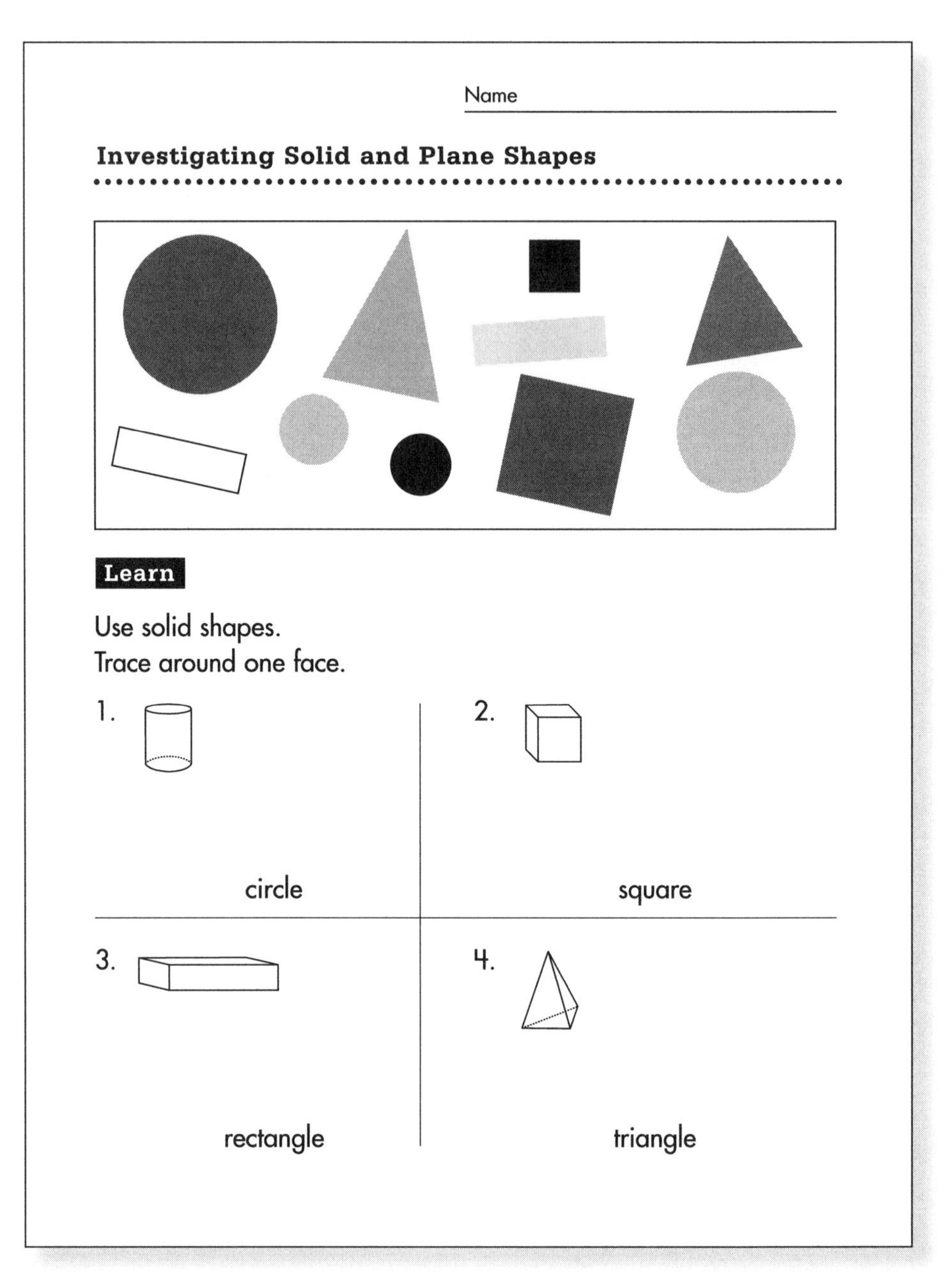
Name

Investigating Solid and Plane Shapes

Learn

Use solid shapes.
Trace around one face.

1. circle
2. square
3. rectangle
4. triangle

NCTM Process Standards Analysis and Focus

The standards analysis examines how the process standards have been incorporated into the above lesson. By increasing the focus on three of the process standards, a more effective and meaningful lesson can be presented. The suggestions offered can help you to think about how this might be accomplished.

Reasoning and Proof The teacher is encouraged to ask children to think about whether given objects roll, stack, or slide. Considering these qualities helps children to develop their ability to recognize attributes of two-dimensional shapes.

Suggestion → **Have children examine and compare a variety of objects that fit a particular classification to identify common physical attributes. Comparing**

Name ______________________

Try

Draw a line from the plane shape to the solid shape.

Think

How many ○ on a ? ______

How many □ on a ? ______

How many △ on a ? ______

many objects and noting their similarities will help children to become aware of the features that comprise that group.

Communication Limited opportunities are included to encourage children to discuss their understandings of solid figures.

Suggestion → **Plan activities that encourage children to discuss geometric solids and their attributes. Allowing time for children to engage in discussions about solid figures will reinforce children's recognition of these shapes.**

Connections In the lesson, children match two-dimensional shapes with three-dimensional figures. An activity suggested in the teacher's notes focuses on connections as children determine which solid forms can roll, stack, or slide.

Suggestion → **Have children explore objects in the classroom that are representative of the solid shapes and consider how their forms are suited to their function. Help children to see how geometric forms are used in the real world. Investigating the attributes of familiar objects allows children to see how mathematics is applied outside the classroom.**

Problem Solving Lesson activities involve recognizing and identifying shapes that match in both size and shape. The lesson does not offer activities that involve problem solving.

Representation Figures are represented by geometric drawings on activity pages. Suggestions in the teacher's notes include having objects representative of solid shapes available for children to see.

The teaching plan that follows shows how the suggestions for increasing the focus on the process standards can be implemented.

Revised Teaching Plan

Materials → Models of geometric solids including a rectangular prism, cube, cylinder, square pyramid, triangular pyramid, cone; familiar everyday objects with shapes that correspond to the geometric solids; empty rectangular boxes and cans in a variety of sizes

DISPLAY A SOLID FIGURE, such as a cube, for the whole class to see. Have children pass the figure around so that everyone can examine it. Allow time for children to make observations and discuss characteristics of the figure. Then challenge children to find objects in the classroom that are representative of the same shape. *As you search the room for a shape like this, what details will you look for? How will you decide if the shape is the same?* If possible, have children bring forward objects to place alongside the solid shape displayed. Have children compare the identified objects to the original. *What is alike about these objects? What is different?* Questions like these focus children's thinking on the attributes of the figure. This, in turn, will help children recognize the attributes that distinguish figures from one another.

FOLLOW A SIMILAR PROCEDURE to introduce the other geometric solids you have gathered for this lesson. Then work with children to create a list of attributes, such as those shown for a box of crayons, for each geometric solid. As you record information, make connections between the real-world objects and the solid ones. This may also be an opportunity to develop more mathematically complex ideas about shapes.

It has flat sides.

It has 6 sides.

Each side looks like a rectangle.

You can stack it.

GUIDE CHILDREN AS THEY IDENTIFY attributes by giving information and asking questions. For example, point to the flat surfaces of a rectangular box. Tell children that the plane or flat surfaces of the box are called *faces*. Work with children to determine the number of faces on the box. *How many faces does a box have? How can we check?* Have children count the 6 faces out loud as a volunteer points to each one. *Are all of the faces the same size? Are they all the same shape? How can we tell?* Next, ask children to identify plane surfaces around the room, such as tops of desks, walls, floors, and book covers.

Draw attention to another box that is noticeably different from the first one. Repeat the questions to confirm children's understanding of the mathematical terms. After looking at a number of rectangular boxes, establish how all have the same number of faces and that all of the faces are in the shape of a rectangle or a square.

Next, make comparisons between rectangular boxes and cubes. Make sure you have a variety of boxes to heighten children's awareness of the distinctions. Work with children to determine the number of faces a cube has. *How many faces does a cube have? How can we check?* Have children count the 6 faces. *What do you notice about the faces of a cube?* Then point out that some boxes have two square faces and others do not. *Can a box have square faces? Can a cube have faces that are not squares?*

NOW, CALL ATTENTION TO THE SQUARE and triangular pyramids. Hold up the figures and turn them around to expose various orientations. *What is the same about these figures? What is different?* If necessary, prompt children by asking questions about the faces. Show the triangular pyramid. *How many faces are there on this figure? Are all of the faces the same shape?* Ask similar questions about the square pyramid. While it is not important for children to be concerned with the names of the different pyramids, it is important for them to realize that not all pyramids are the same.

f.y.i.

A pyramid is named according to the shape of its base. For example, a square pyramid has a square base, a triangular pyramid has a base in the shape of a triangle, the base of a pentagonal pyramid is a pentagon, and so on.

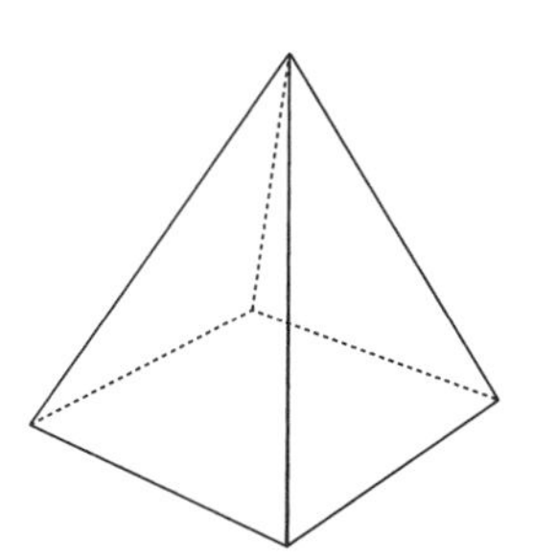

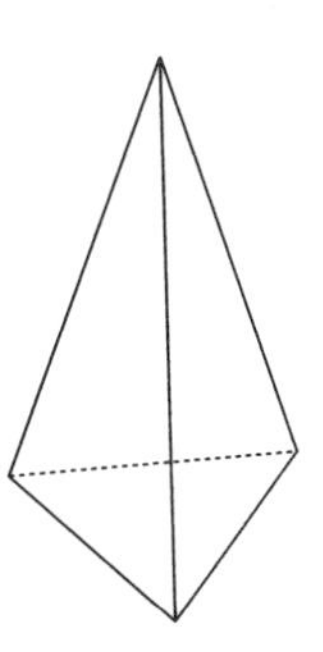

Connect the concept of faces with other geometric figures. Hold up a cylinder. Have children pass the figure around so that everyone can examine it. *What is the name of this shape? How did we say we could identify a face on one of our figures?* (A face is flat.) *How many faces does a cylinder have?* (2) Point to the lateral surface or side of the figure. *Is this a face?* (No.) *Why?* (It isn't flat; it's round.) Hold up a cone, which has only one face, and ask similar questions.

What Might Happen . . . What to Do

Because most children are familiar with party hats and ice-cream cones, they may be confused when hearing that a cone has a circular face. After all, in their experiences, the opening of a party hat is where their head goes and the opening of an ice-cream cone is where the ice cream goes! Point out that while those objects are, in fact, cone shaped, when we talk about cones in math we are talking about solid figures with surfaces that don't have openings. Children can trace the face of this shape to confirm this information.

Place a solid figure into a paper bag. Ask a volunteer to reach into the bag and feel the shape. Have the volunteer describe what he/she feels. Instruct children to close their eyes and imagine the shape as it is being described. Then ask children to identify the shape. Repeat the activity with other shapes.

Conclude the lesson with a discussion about whether shapes can stack, roll, and/or slide. As children offer responses about each shape, ask them to explain their thinking and tell how they might prove their answers. This is another opportunity to invoke reasoning and to help children understand how mathematics relates to the real world. *Why don't we use boxes or cubes as wheels on bikes or cars?* (They don't roll.) *Why do you think cereal comes in boxes? How does that shape help a storeowner?* (Boxes can be stacked on shelves.) *What about food that comes in cans such as soup?* (Cans can be stacked, too.)

As a follow-up assignment, you might encourage children to look for representations of geometric solids in magazines and catalogs at home and bring them to school to share with the class.

Student Pages

Children should now be ready to complete exercises similar to those on the reduced student pages.

Assessment

As children identified and described items representing geometric solids that were found in the classroom, there were opportunities to assess their understanding of solid and plane shapes. As children participated in whole-group discussions, opportunities surfaced to assess the depth of their understanding about the relationship between geometric solids and their faces.

NCTM Standards Summary

Throughout the lesson, children were encouraged to make conjectures about geometric shapes and offer details to support their thinking. Many connections between the mathematical ideas and everyday experiences were pointed out. Small and whole-class discussions offered a meaningful context for children to hear and use specialized vocabulary as they described shapes and their faces. Allowing time for children to express their ideas provided a valuable opportunity for them to develop and clarify their understanding of geometric forms.

Standard 4 **Measurement**

AT THE FIRST GRADE LEVEL, measurement includes work with measuring weight, estimating and measuring length, and measuring perimeter and area of figures. Our lessons are derived from these important topics, and include a lesson on determining the heaviest object in a group of objects, a lesson on measuring with nonstandard units of length, a lesson that explores area, and a lesson on estimating and measuring with metric units of length.

Three lessons model how the process standards can be used to teach content. A fourth lesson is a hypothetical textbook lesson that we have revised to be more standards based. These four lessons do not represent the entire curriculum, but rather provide glimpses of how, with a more concentrated effort to incorporate the process standards, better mathematics teaching and learning can be achieved.

In one lesson we have chosen, children determine the heaviest object from a group of objects. The process standards of problem solving, reasoning and proof, and communication are important here as children are presented a group of objects and asked to determine which of them is the heaviest.

Another lesson we have chosen is one in which children measure length using nonstandard units. Using the process standards of problem solving, communication, and connections, children solve problems that require them to find length. They discuss their methods and begin to realize the importance of having a standard unit.

A third lesson we have chosen is one that explores how to measure the area of rectangular regions. Children are presented a problem within the context of a story. Problem solving is required here at several levels, as children develop a plan to solve the problem and how to carry out this plan. Communication is also very important as children discuss their plans for solving and interpret their results.

The hypothetical textbook lesson we have chosen to revise is one that has children estimating and measuring length using the metric units centimeters and decimeters. Through increased emphasis on representation, communication, and reasoning and proof, children gain a better sense of just how long each unit is, and how to better use a metric ruler. Children also get more opportunities to discuss the measures.

Standard 4 Lessons

Comparing Weights

Measuring with Nonstandard Units of Length

Exploring Area

Estimating and Measuring Metric Units of Length

Comparing Weights

Introduction

Objective → Children will determine the heaviest object from a group of objects.

Context → Children know the terms *heavier* and *lighter.* They have had experience with balances. This lesson might be a last lesson in a unit on weight.

NCTM Standards Focus

This lesson is different from typical lessons on measuring and comparing weights. Asking children to compare the weights of two objects and decide which is heavier and which is lighter is as far as most lessons go. This lesson, while focusing on comparing weights, is really a problem-solving activity. Children are required to use their problem-solving skills and their reasoning and proof skills and to communicate effectively as they explore comparing weights of objects.

Problem Solving Given a set of four identical looking bags of different weights and a balance with only two pans, children determine which bag is the heaviest. They work in groups to develop their own strategies for solving the problem.

Reasoning and Proof Children develop their own theories about how to determine the heaviest object. They test their ideas in order to justify their conclusions.

Communication Children discuss ways to solve the problem in small groups. They present their solutions to the class and listen to the solutions of other groups.

Teaching Plan

Materials → Student pages 100–101; for each group, four bags of marbles, beans, or other filler that are relatively close in weight and a pan balance

ALLOW CHILDREN TO WORK on this problem-solving activity in small groups. Give each group a pan balance and four bags, labeled A, B, C, and D. Children should not be able to see inside the bags. Their goal is simply to determine which of the four bags is the heaviest.

This problem-solving activity might initially seem difficult for the children, as there are four bags but only two pans on the balance. For children having a hard time getting started, suggest they begin by weighing two bags. *What will you learn by weighing two of the bags?* (That one is heavier than the other.)

Observe the children as they work in their groups. Group discussions should focus on how to keep track of the results and how to be sure that the one bag they think is the heaviest really is the heaviest.

Two questions you might ask as you circulate among the groups are: *What did you learn from that last weighing? What is your plan for what two bags to weigh next?* These questions will keep children focused on the goal, as well as provide you with some insight into the intermediate steps a particular group uses. Children's responses will allow you to assess children's progress through the activity.

Methods Children Might Use

- Children might first weigh two of the bags and identify the heavier bag. Next, they might weigh the other two bags, and again identify the heavier bag. Then they might weigh the two heavier bags. In this instance, the heavier bag would be the heaviest bag of the four.
- Children might weigh two of the bags, and keep the heavier bag on its pan. Next, they might replace the lighter bag with one of the other two bags, again keeping the heavier bag on its pan. Finally, they might replace the lighter bag with the fourth bag. The heavier of the two bags is the heaviest bag of the four.
- Children might weigh all possible pairs of bags and record each result. Then they would use their logical reasoning skills to determine which bag is the heaviest.
- Children might randomly weigh different pairs of bags until they notice that one bag in particular always seems heavier than the bag it is compared against.

Once children have determined which bag is the heaviest, have them present their results to the class. This discussion will really bring out the reasons for the emphasis on the process standards. Children have to communicate clearly their methods for determining the heaviest bag. The other children have to evaluate and question those methods if they are not satisfied that the group has proven which bag is the heaviest. This discussion incorporates both the reasoning and the proof aspects of the process standard. You may have to help children evaluate groups' methods, as they might not entirely comprehend the group's presentation, nor possess enough language to question effectively.

Depending on the amount of time remaining, you might want children to do some additional activities. Some options follow.

Activity 1

If you feel that your children are not ready for more advanced thinking, and could benefit from another activity at the same level, you can have children do the same activity, but this time determine which bag is the lightest.

Activity 2

If your children are ready for more advanced thinking, you can have the children order the four bags from heaviest to lightest. Children could take a couple of approaches to this problem. One way would be that they could first find the heaviest bag, as in the original activity, then find the heaviest of the three remaining bags, then the heavier of the other two bags.

Activity 3

Give the children five bags, and have them determine which one is the heaviest.

Activity 4

Give children five bags and have them rank the bags from heaviest to lightest. The point here is *How much more work does the one extra bag create?*

Student Pages

Student page 100 contains reasoning exercises similar to the problem-solving activity in the lesson, but using only three bags. Student page 101 contains some reasoning exercises similar to the problem-solving activity, using four bags.

Assessment

As the children worked in their groups, you were able to observe how each was able to participate and how well groups were able to work together. You also observed how well their problem-solving skills were developing and evaluated the kinds of reasoning that was taking place. As children presented their methods, you evaluated their communication skills and the validity of their reasoning.

NCTM Standards Summary

This problem-solving activity really brought out what the process standards are about. Children were presented with an interesting problem to solve, and had to use their reasoning skills and their communication skills to come up with a solution. It is these kinds of experiences that are so valuable to children, especially at the early grade levels, where these skills are not often emphasized.

Answers

Page 100

1. A
2. B
3. C

Page 101

1. A
2. B
3. A

Name

Comparing Weights

Use the clues.
Decide which bag is the heaviest.

❶ Which bag is the heaviest? ____________

❷ Which bag is the heaviest? ____________

❸ Which bag is the heaviest? ____________

Name ____________________

Comparing Weights

Use the clues.
Decide which bag is the heaviest.

❶ Which bag is the heaviest? ____________

❷ Which bag is the heaviest? ____________

❸ Which bag is the heaviest? ____________

Measuring with Nonstandard Units of Length

Introduction

Objective → Children will measure length using nonstandard units.

Context → Children have experienced measurement in many real-world contexts. They use comparative terms like *biggest, longest, shortest,* and *tallest* to talk about measurable attributes. In future lessons, children will continue to measure with nonstandard units and then standard units to quantify lengths.

NCTM Standards Focus

When we want to know how big or how long something is, we need to use a quantifiable unit. Continued experiences with measuring length using nonstandard units helps children develop an understanding of units of measure. This standards-based lesson enables children to learn how to repeat a single unit to measure length. It helps them build a foundation for later work with standard measurement tools, such as rulers.

Problem Solving Children measure length with nonstandard units in order to solve a problem that requires finding and comparing lengths. In the process of measuring, children must figure out how to resolve discrepancies related to their methods and the units of measure.

Communication One reason we measure in units, whether nonstandard or standard, is to communicate about measurements. In this lesson, children discuss and compare their measuring methods and results.

Connections Through experience with measuring length, children call on and develop their spatial sense and their counting ability.

Teaching Plan

Materials → Student pages 106–107; a number line; 3 or 4 of the following: connecting cubes, color tiles, connecting links, dominoes, craft sticks, large paper clips, toothpicks; chart paper

SHOW THE CHILDREN the number line and explain that you would like to post some number lines like this one in the classroom. You want to put them in places where everyone can see them and touch them. *What places in our classroom would work? Why do you think so?*

Rather than asking whether a certain location would be appropriate, notice how the first question leaves children with an open-ended, problem-solving opportunity. The next question also requires children to problem-solve.

Together, brainstorm and list some places in the classroom where number lines would fit and be accessible. You may need to suggest some possibilities to get the children started, such as along the lengths of tables or along a section of the bulletin board. Explain that you would like to find places that are pretty close to the length of the number line.

How can we be sure that the places we're thinking of are the right length for the number line? Children may suggest that you hold the number line up to the different places. Let them know that that's a good way to compare length, but ask them to think of another way. *Suppose another teacher needs to use the number line today. How can we compare the number line to places in our classroom if we don't actually have it to look at?*

If the children don't suggest finding a way to measure the length of the number line, bring it up. *What would be a good way to figure out the length of the number line?* Accept children's suggestions. If no one suggests lining up and counting units, ask children how using cubes could help.

If measuring with nonstandard units is new to your children, model using cubes (or another unit) to measure a short length such as the length of a new pencil. Line up cubes along the pencil. *How many cubes long is this pencil?* Together, count the cubes. *How could you use the cubes to help you figure out where the number line could go?* Lead children to see that they can measure the number line with cubes and then measure places in the classroom with cubes and compare the lengths.

HAVE A FEW VOLUNTEERS work with you to measure the number line using cubes. Model the process of laying the line out on a flat surface and lining up the cubes carefully, end-to-end, from one end of the number line to the other. If the measure is not an exact number of cubes, explain that you will use the closest number. Post the measure on chart paper: _____ cubes.

Call on new volunteers to measure with the remaining objects you have provided as units of measure. Add these measures to the chart paper, including the unit for each one. If children use connecting links or paper clips, show them how to place the units end-to-end, without linking them, to avoid overlapping the units.

TELL CHILDREN that they are going to measure places in the room to find places that are about the same length as the number line. Point to the chart. *What do you notice about these numbers? Are they all measures of the same number line? Why aren't they all the same?*

For children who are ready to take a step forward in their thinking about measurement, this discussion can help them consider the size of the unit being used. As they continue to share and compare measurements, a few children may even realize that the larger the unit, the fewer units are needed to measure a given length.

f.y.i.

There are a number of good children's books about linear measurement. A few examples are *How Big Is a Foot?* by Rolf Myller, *Inch by Inch* by Leo Lionni, and *The Tiny Seed* by Eric Carle. Read these books aloud to your class to help reinforce children's understanding of measurement of length.

GO OVER STUDENT PAGE 106 with the children and discuss how they will use it to record their work. Divide the class into small groups or pairs. Each group or pair should use one of the nonstandard units that were used for the number line. They'll use that unit to find the length of one place in the classroom and compare that length to the length of the number line. Be sure to have two or more groups measure the same length using different units of measure. This will give children an additional opportunity to compare measurements.

Each child should record his/her group's work on student page 106. At this time, children should answer all but the last question. Ask the groups to keep their measuring materials intact, so that they can show and compare their work.

Have the children share their measurements. Ask groups who have measured the same lengths using different units of measure to compare their results. *How many cubes long is the table? How many dominoes long is the table? Why do you think Kate and Mario's number is larger than John and Leah's? The two pairs measured the same table; should they have the same results?* The first two questions are fairly standard, but the last two questions require that children communicate their thinking about measurement.

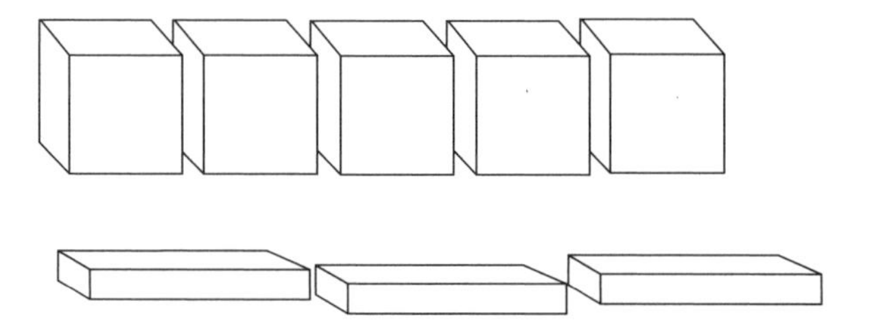

READ THE LAST QUESTION on page 106, and display the chart paper with the measurements of the number line. *Kate and Mario measured the table with cubes. They want to know if the table is the same length as the number line. What should they do?* Elicit from children the idea that to compare two lengths, the lengths have to be measured in the same units. Have children discuss this idea until they are ready to answer the last question on page 106.

Have children do student page 107 another day, or at home. If they use page 107 as homework, you might have them first work in pairs to answer the riddles. Be sure they have access to uniform objects to use as their units of measure.

Student Pages

Student page 106 is a recording sheet for the classroom measurement activity. Student page 107 gives children further practice in measuring length with nonstandard units.

Assessment

This lesson provided an opportunity for you to assess children's understanding of measuring length with nonstandard units and of comparing lengths. The children's work during the lesson and on student page 106 offered opportunities to assess their developing understanding of the concept of linear measurement. As they worked, you could note their strategies for making measurements and for counting and keeping track of the number of units used. In discussion, you noted their ideas about different units of measure and what they must do to compare two lengths.

NCTM Standards Summary

Children built on and extended their informal knowledge of measurement in this lesson. Their work was purposeful—they used measurement to solve a problem. In addition, they solved problems arising from their methods and their use of different units of measure. They communicated their results to each other and discussed the steps they took to problem solve. These experiences with measuring length also connected to children's spatial sense, counting skill, and ability in addition and subtraction.

Answers

Page 106
1–5. Answers will vary.

Page 107
1. book
2. shoe
3. pencil

Name ____________________

Measuring with Nonstandard Units of Length

Use pictures, numbers, and words to answer the questions.

1. What unit are you using to measure?

____

2. What item are you measuring?

____

3. How long is the item you measured?

____

4. What did you do to get the measurement?

____

____

____

5. Do you think this would be a good place for a number line? Why or why not?

____

____

____

Name

Measuring with Nonstandard Units of Length

Solve each riddle. Measure each length.

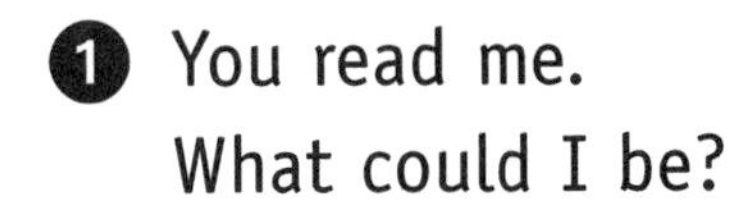

1. You read me.
What could I be?

How long am I?

2. You wear me on your foot.
What could I be?

How long am I?

3. You use me to write.
You are probably holding me now.
What could I be?

How long am I?

Exploring Area

Introduction

Objective → Children will explore area and use nonstandard units to measure area.

Context → Children have explored perimeter. In future lessons, children will focus on how to measure area using standard units.

NCTM Standards Focus

Children are not always presented with a reason, or a context, in which to explore area. Sometimes standard units of measure can hinder children from being able to focus on what area means. A standards-based lesson would take these things into account. By incorporating the process standards, a better lesson for exploring area can be presented.

Problem Solving Children investigate the problem of how to compare areas of different shapes and work together to develop a strategy. In carrying out their strategy, they encounter and solve other problems, such as how to keep track of the tiles they have counted.

Communication Children use nonstandard units to communicate about and compare the areas of rectangles. They share their thinking about the difficulties of comparing areas, their strategies, and their results.

Connections Children connect geometry and number to measurement as they put together smaller tiles to equal a larger shape and then tell how many tiles cover the larger shape.

Teaching Plan

Materials → Student pages 112–113; color tiles or inch squares of colored paper; yellow construction paper

Preparation → For each pair of children, cut four rectangles from the yellow paper in these sizes: 12" × 2", 5" × 5", 9" × 3", and 8" × 4".

GATHER THE CHILDREN TOGETHER in your classroom meeting area. Pose a problem, such as the story problem provided here, so children will have a purpose for comparing different areas.

> One day, 2 little field mice smelled something absolutely wonderful! They followed their noses through a field, under a fence, and into a backyard. Soon they were squeezing under a kitchen door. And there, in the kitchen, the field mice saw 4 big beautiful slices of flat bread. "Let's bring all the flat bread home to our families!" they squeaked. "We can only carry 1 piece of flat bread at a time, so we'll have to make 4 trips." The mice were excited; their whiskers twitched at the very idea of all that delicious flat bread. But then, something moved under the table! The something was big and furry. What do you think it was?

A cat was sleeping under the table! "Well," said one mouse, "we can't come back here for all the pieces of flat bread. If Mr. Cat wakes up, we will be in BIG TROUBLE!" "You're right," said the other mouse. "We can't come back, but we can take one piece of flat bread home with us now. Let's take the biggest piece."

Show each of the 4 prepared rectangles to represent the slices of bread.

- One piece was long and skinny. (Show the 12" × 2" rectangle.)
- One was shaped like a square. (Show the 5" × 5" rectangle.)
- The other 2 looked almost, but not quite, the same. (Show the 9" × 3" and the 8" × 4" rectangle.)

ARRANGE THE RECTANGLES so everyone can see them. Remind children that the mice wanted to take the biggest piece. *Which piece do you think is the biggest? How can you find out?*

Children may want to guess which piece is the largest. Accept their guesses, but guide them to consider how they can find out for sure. Children's suggestions will probably include comparing areas by placing the pieces on top of one another. Try out their suggestions. In the case of placing pieces on top of one another, help the children see that it is difficult to compare the size of the pieces because of the differences in shape.

If no one suggests it, or if the children aren't sure what to do, show them the color tiles (or paper one-inch squares). *Could you use these to figure out which rectangle is the biggest? How?*

ENCOURAGE CHILDREN TO SEE that the tiles can be used to cover the pieces of "flat bread." You might start by placing a few tiles on one piece. Together, talk about how the tiles can help you find out how big the piece of flat bread is. During this discussion, perhaps as you restate children's ideas, use the word *area* in context, and point out the enclosed region of the shape. Do not refer to the tiles as being one-inch squares. Children should focus on placing and counting units to compare areas, not on actual measurements.

Explain to children that they are going to try to figure out the area of this piece. They need to see how many squares or tiles will cover the rectangle. Ask a volunteer to help you finish covering the rectangle with tiles. Talk about this process. *How should the tiles be arranged? Should the whole rectangle be covered? Why? What happens if you leave spaces?* Count the number of tiles that covered the rectangle.

What Might Happen . . . What to Do

Some children might focus on one dimension of the shapes. "This one is longer, so it must be bigger." Show children a long, narrow rectangle and a medium-sized square. Point out that comparing one dimension could show the rectangle to be bigger, but by comparing the other dimension, the square would be bigger. Both dimensions have to be considered.

Pair children and distribute 4 rectangles and color tiles to each pair. Instruct pairs to find out how many square tiles it takes to cover each rectangular piece of flat bread. They can then decide which piece is the biggest. Tell the children to be sure to record their results.

CIRCULATE AMONG THE CHILDREN as they work. Ask questions to help them focus on the concept of area. *Once you've placed the tiles on the rectangle, how can you count how many tiles there are? How can you decide which rectangle is bigger? Which piece of flat bread would the mice bring home? Why?*

What Might Happen . . . What to Do

Some children might have difficulty counting the correct number of tiles due to skipping tiles or counting some tiles twice. You might need to model touching and moving each tile aside as it is counted, or suggest skip counting by the number of tiles in each row or column.

f.y.i.

Consider having the children write a story about how the mice decided which piece of bread to bring home. Or ask them to make up an ending to the story.

BRING THE CHILDREN TOGETHER to share their results. *Do you all agree on which piece of bread is the largest? How many tiles did it take to cover each rectangle?* If there are discrepancies, work together to cover the rectangles and recount the tiles. Talk about why children may have arrived at different answers. Remind children of important measurement concepts:

- Align tiles so there are no gaps or overlaps.
- Count each unit only once.
- Keep track when you count the tiles.

Conclude the lesson by assigning the student pages. You might want to use the pages on the following day.

Extension

Have children try to cover an area using shapes from a set of pattern blocks; they should use just one shape for each measurement. Then have children try covering an area with pennies. Draw attention to the gaps that result when using pennies.

Student Pages

Student page 112 has children predict the relative areas of three rectangles, then measure each with color tiles. On student page 113, children use color tiles to measure the areas of real objects in the classroom. (Note that the tiles may not cover the regions exactly. Encourage children to think about how they can deal with this situation. Some children may be able to count "halves" of units, but others may only consider whole units.)

Assessment

As children compared rectangles, you could note whether they focused on the length or width of a rectangle rather than on its area. The children's work offered opportunities to assess their developing understanding of counting the number of squares to find area and their strategies for counting and keeping track of square units.

NCTM Standards Summary

In this lesson, children investigated the concept of area and developed skill in measuring area. They solved the problem of determining the largest area by using square tiles to measure the areas of different rectangles. They communicated the decisions they made and their strategies for measuring area. They related geometric ideas to measurement as they covered rectangles with square tiles and put together smaller shapes to make a larger shape. They used the cardinal meaning of number to describe how many tiles covered the rectangles.

Answers

Page 112
Answers will vary. Check children's prediction of area with their actual measurement.

Page 113
Answers will vary.

Name ______________________

Exploring Area

Look at each rectangle.

1. Which rectangle do you think has the largest area? __________

A

B

C

2. Cover each rectangle with tiles. Count the tiles to find the area.

3. Write how many tiles you used.

Rectangle A __________

Rectangle B __________

Rectangle C __________

4. Which rectangle has the largest area? __________

5. How do you know?

____

____

Name ____________________

Exploring Area

Find these things in your classroom:

- a piece of construction paper
- a file card
- a book

Measure the area of the construction paper with tiles.

How many tiles did you use? __________

Measure the area of the file card with tiles.

How many tiles did you use? __________

Measure the area of the book cover with tiles.

How many tiles did you use? __________

Estimating and Measuring Metric Units of Length

Objective → Children will estimate and measure length in centimeters (cm) and decimeters (dm).

Context → Children have discussed the concept of length and have used nonstandard units such as paper clips to measure objects. Future lessons may include estimating and comparing weight.

Name ____________

Estimating and Measuring Metric Units of Length

Learn

1 cm

1 centimeter

1 centimeter can be written **1 cm.**

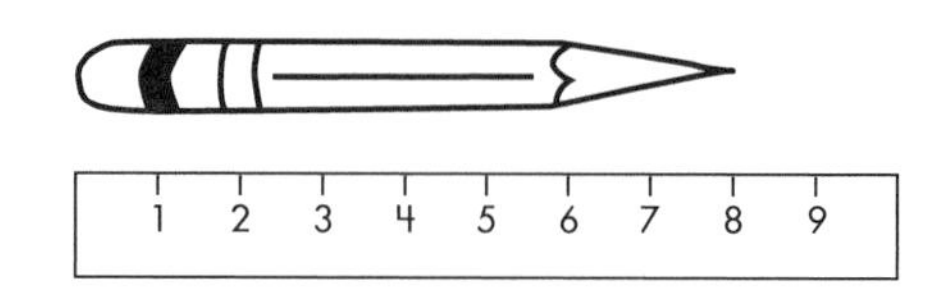

This pencil is about 8 centimeters long. 8 centimeters can be written **8 cm.**

Estimate how long each object is.
Measure the object.

Object	My Estimate	My Measurement
1.	about ___ cm	about ___ cm
2.	about ___ cm	about ___ cm
3.	about ___ cm	about ___ cm
4.	about ___ cm	about ___ cm

NCTM Process Standards Analysis and Focus

The standards analysis examines how the process standards have been incorporated into the above lesson. By increasing the focus on three of the process standards, a more effective and meaningful lesson can be presented. The suggestions offered can help you to think about how this might be accomplished.

Representation Student pages display pictures of a ruler marked in centimeters along with various objects to estimate and measure. Demonstrating how to use a ruler is called out in the teacher notes.

Suggestion → **Give meaning to the metric lengths used in the lesson by familiarizing children with objects that represent the units. Such references will provide a basis for comparison against**

Name ____________________

Find the object.
Estimate how long it is.
Measure the object.

	My Estimate	My Measurement
1.	about ___ cm	about ___ cm
2.	about ___ cm	about ___ cm
3.	about ___ cm	about ___ cm

1 2 3 4 5 6 7 8 9 10

10 centimeters is equal to 1 **decimeter**.

4. What are some things that are shorter than 1 decimeter?

____

5. What are some things that are longer than 1 decimeter?

____

which estimates can be made. Take time to discuss and demonstrate how to use a ruler to measure length.

Communication Communication is limited to questions that appear at the end of the lesson when children are asked to talk about objects that may be longer or shorter than a decimeter.

Suggestion → **Allocate time for meaningful discussions that encourage children to talk about how they estimate and measure the length of an object. Allowing time for children to describe strategies enhances their understanding of mathematical concepts.**

Reasoning and Proof While judgment needs to be exercised when estimating lengths, children are not asked to explain any decision-making steps.

Suggestion → **Provide activities that help children to build references by which to judge lengths. Allow time for children to explain their thinking along the way. Have children estimate and then check their estimates by doing the actual measuring.**

Connections Using metric units is related to previous learning experiences with nonstandard units of measure. At the beginning of the lesson, a pictured object is connected to its measure on a ruler.

Problem Solving Estimating measurements requires making comparisons but does not involve problem solving.

The teaching plan that follows shows how the suggestions for increasing the focus on the process standards can be implemented.

Revised Teaching Plan

Materials → Metric rulers marked off in centimeters only, overhead projector, centimeter ruler for the overhead, paper decimeter strips (paper or tag board cut into 10-cm strips), classroom objects in a variety of lengths

INTRODUCE THE CONCEPT OF CENTIMETERS by telling children that centimeters are used to measure how long things are. Make a connection between using centimeters and using the various nonstandard units of measure children are familiar with for measuring length, such as paper clips, connecting cubes, and hands. Discuss the fact that unlike these nonstandard units, centimeters are a unit for measuring length that is used throughout the world and that they are always the same size. Ask children to consider why a standard unit of measurement would be important and, conversely, why measuring objects with nonstandard units would be problematic? *Can you imagine trying to buy shoes without having standard shoe sizes? What about building a house and not having yards, feet, and inches to measure the lengths of wood?*

Distribute centimeter rulers. Explain that a ruler is a tool used to measure length. Draw children's attention to the markings on the ruler. Tell children that all the markings are the same distance apart and that it is exactly the same distance from the 2 to the 3 as it is from the 6 to the 7. Encourage children to verify this. Write the term *centimeter* and the abbreviation *cm* on the board. Explain that each unit on this ruler is called a centimeter and that a centimeter is a standard unit for measuring length; in other words, a centimeter is always the same.

Have children hold up a pinkie finger. Relate that for many people, the width of this finger is *about* one centimeter. Allow time for children to measure the width of their little fingers with the centimeter ruler. If necessary, use the overhead projector to demonstrate how to place the pinkie finger between cm marks. *Do you think all little fingers are about one centimeter wide? Why or why not? Is your little finger about a centimeter wide? What about your other fingers? Do you have another finger that is about the same width as the centimeter space?*

Work with children to develop a sense of familiarity with centimeter lengths. *What do you think two centimeters would look like? Show me by holding up your thumb and pointer fingers. What helped you to know? Do you see something in the classroom that you think represents this length? How can you check?*

Display small objects that vary in length. Hold up each object, one at a time, for children to see. Ask children if they think the object is about 1 cm, 2 cm, 5 cm, 10 cm, or longer. Allow time for children to discuss their estimates by sharing how they determined the length of each object. If possible, place an object on the overhead projector and model how to measure it to check an estimate. Demonstrate how to align the edge of the object with the zero point on the ruler when measuring. These types of activities reinforce how to use a ruler and provide practice in reading the measure.

DISTRIBUTE DECIMETER STRIPS. Allow time for children to measure the strips with their centimeter rulers.

Write the term *decimeter* and the abbreviation *dm* on the board. Introduce the term and explain that these strips are referred to as decimeter strips. *What do you notice about the decimeter strip? How many centimeters do you think it takes to make one decimeter?* Explain to children that the decimeter strips are 10 cm long. Use the overhead projector to reinforce how to align the edge of a strip with the zero point on the ruler to measure it. Ask children to use their rulers to measure their strips. Also, model and have children use their fingers to count off centimeters on their strips.

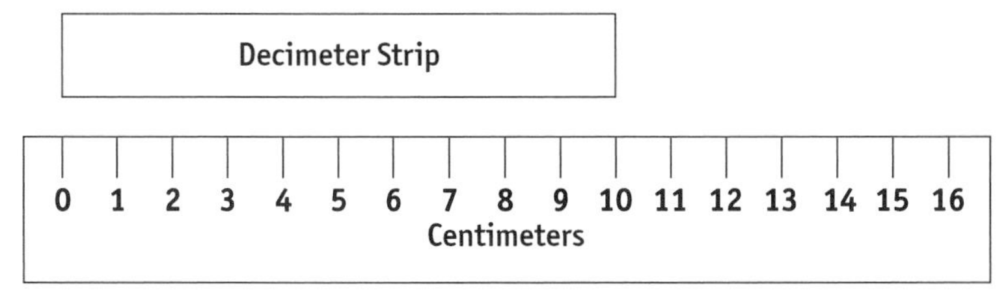

Does anybody know what half of 10 is? If the decimeter strip is ten centimeters long, how many centimeters will half of the strip be? Show children how to fold the strip into two equal parts of 5 centimeters. Confirm that from the edge to the fold is 5 centimeters.

Have pairs of children work together to relate both decimeter and 5-cm measures to parts of their hands. Suggest that they measure from the heel of their hand to a fingertip to see if it is close to a decimeter. *Is one of your fingers about five centimeters long?* Encourage partners to discuss strategies; this provides an opportunity for children to use the language of mathematics as well as to acquire greater understanding of the concept.

WORK WITH CHILDREN to help them become more familiar with decimeters. Use both the centimeter ruler and decimeter strip to demonstrate how centimeters are smaller units and decimeters are longer units made up of 10 centimeters. Talk about things that might be easier to measure with each tool; shorter objects should be measured with centimeter rulers, longer objects with decimeter strips.

Helping children to develop mental images of the units of measure is important because the better able they are to visualize the length, the more accurate their estimates will be. Ask children to think of some objects they might use as references to represent a centimeter and a decimeter when they are estimating. Such objects as a pencil, chalkboard eraser, or book might be suggested.

Highlight strategies for children to use when estimating the length of an object:

- Picturing the length of a ruler mentally
- Using a reference such as an object with a known measurement that is about the same length and comparing it to the new object
- Comparing an object to a known larger object and saying that it looks like about half
- Using an object with a smaller known measurement as a comparison and using multiples of the smaller object because the item looks like two or three of them

Take time to talk through and demonstrate the different strategies. These activities not only help to reinforce the size of standard units but also help children to begin to see the practical applications of knowing approximately how long specific objects are.

CONCLUDE THE LESSON by having children estimate and measure several objects that you have selected in advance. Include objects that are two or three decimeters long. Instruct children to first determine whether to measure with centimeters (cm) or decimeters (dm); next, estimate the object's length; and last, use a ruler or decimeter strip to measure the object. Plan time for children to share and compare their findings. In your discussions, reinforce procedures such as lining objects up with the ruler and carefully reading numbers on the ruler.

What Might Happen . . . What to Do

Children might be disappointed because their estimates do not match the exact measurements. Discuss the purpose of estimating—that an estimate is not intended to be exact but rather to provide an idea of about how long something is. Give examples of situations when estimates are appropriate as opposed to situations when an exact measurement is required. Assure children that the more they practice estimating and checking to see how close they are, the more accurate they will become. The goal is to become a better estimator.

Student Pages

Children are now ready to complete exercises similar to those on the reduced student pages.

Assessment

Opportunities existed to assess children's abilities to use centimeters and decimeters to estimate and measure as they identified various classroom objects. Listening to children's responses during whole-class discussions provided an opportunity to evaluate the strategies they employed as they estimated and measured lengths.

NCTM Standards Summary

Children developed better understanding of centimeters and decimeters by determining familiar objects that represented those lengths. Familiar references offered a basis for comparison by which estimates then could be made. Children were asked to articulate reasons behind their decisions as they estimated the lengths of objects. Modeling specific strategies gave children methods to apply when estimating lengths. Experiences such as these offered a natural context in which children could use the language of estimation and measurement.

Standard 5 **Data Analysis and Probability**

AT THE FIRST GRADE LEVEL, data analysis and probability includes a lot of work with different representations of data, both graphical and statistical, and probability concepts. Our lessons are derived from these important topics, and include a lesson on representing data in a glyph, a lesson in which children predict outcomes, a lesson in which children identify the mode of a data set, and a lesson on interpreting bar graphs.

Three lessons model how the process standards can be used to teach content. A fourth lesson is a hypothetical textbook lesson that we have revised to be more standards based. These four lessons do not represent the entire curriculum, but rather provide glimpses of how, with a more concentrated effort to incorporate the process standards, better mathematics teaching and learning can be achieved.

In one lesson we have chosen children collect and represent data by making a glyph. By basing this lesson on the process standards of representation, communication, and connections, children discuss the information shown in the glyph. They compare and describe the data. In this lesson, each glyph represents a collection of data rather than just one piece.

Another lesson we have chosen focuses on probability. Through the process standards of reasoning and proof, communication, and problem solving, children make predictions based on the contents of a bag. Children perform simple probability experiments to test their predictions. They develop the concept of likely and unlikely.

A third lesson we have chosen is a lesson in which children identify the mode of a set of data. By incorporating the process standards of representation and communication, children also generate their own data, show the data in a physical graph and a line plot, and use the line plot to determine the mode.

The hypothetical textbook lesson we have chosen to revise is a lesson that has children interpreting the information contained in a bar graph. Through better incorporation of the process standards of communication, representation, and reasoning and proof, children examine both horizontal and vertical bar graphs. Rather than asking questions about a singular bit of information, questions are presented that require children to make comparisons, interpretations, and predictions.

Standard 5 Lessons

Representing Data

Predicting Outcomes

Recognizing the Mode of a Data Set

Interpreting Bar Graphs

Representing Data

Introduction

Objective → Children will collect and represent data by making glyphs and will use the data (glyphs) to answer questions about themselves and the class as a whole.

Context → Children have followed directions to position geometric shapes. They will continue to use the language for following directions and apply it in new ways as they move from geometry to data.

NCTM Standards Focus

First graders are focused on themselves and their immediate surroundings. This lesson encourages children to create face glyphs of symbols that represent data about themselves. Children then use their completed face glyphs as data to create graphs representing information about the class and answer questions about the graphs they create.

Representation Children use facial features to represent elements in the key of glyphs that provide data about themselves. They then sort their glyphs in various ways to create bar graphs that show different facts about the group.

Communication Children discuss and explain the information that their glyphs represent. They compare and describe the data they have sorted according to given parameters.

Connections Children connect symbols on the glyph to the information that it represents. They sort their glyphs into related groups to create bar graphs.

Teaching Plan

Materials → Student pages 126–127; chart paper; crayons; large paper plates; scissors; glue; a set of pre-cut materials from student pages for teacher demonstration

IN THIS LESSON CHILDREN will be making face glyphs using paper plates and features (eyes, noses, etc.) cut out from the student pages. First lead the children in a discussion to collect and organize data into a legend. Then demonstrate how to make a paper plate face glyph for the class using data about yourself. You may wish to make your sample glyph ahead of time.

Ask children what types of information would help them learn more about each other. As children share their ideas, list their suggestions on chart paper. Be sure that the following questions are included.

Are you a boy or a girl?
Do you have brothers and/or sisters?
What type of activity do you like for recess?
What kinds of pets do you have?
How do you get to school?

When the list has been completed, tell the children that they will be making face glyphs, special faces that will give others information about themselves. They will use eyes, a nose, a mouth, and bows to make their face glyphs. Explain that you will make a sample to show them what to do. You will answer some of the questions on the list to find out what symbols to use for the glyph.

f.y.i.

Glyphs are symbols that represent information.

CREATE A LEGEND for the face glyph on chart paper. First, copy the *Information* column from the legend below and add any information gathered in your class discussion that should be included. Then, select descriptions you will use to make your sample glyph. Explain that symbols are used in the legend to identify the data being represented. For example, you might drive to school, have a sister, and so on. For each description you select, write the symbol used as shown below. Also place a symbol pre-cut from the student pages next to the written description for visual reinforcement. Complete your sample glyph by placing the appropriate cut-out symbols. Then ask children to read your glyph to tell facts about you. *How does the legend help us understand the face glyph?*

Complete the legend by placing a written description and symbol to represent each entry in the *Information* column. The completed legend should look like this:

Information	Symbol/Legend
1. Girl or Boy	
girl	bow on hair
boy	bow under chin
2. Family	
brothers	blue bow
sisters	green bow
brother(s) and sister(s)	red bow
only child	yellow bow
3. Recess	
likes to play a game	smile/big
likes to play on the equipment	smile/small
likes to run around with friends	jagged smile
4. Pets	
no pets	star eyes
dog(s) or cat(s)	circle eyes
other kinds of pets	triangle eyes
5. Getting to School	
rides a bus	circle nose
rides in a car	square nose
rides a bicycle	triangle nose
walks	rectangle nose

Distribute student pages 126 and 127, a large paper plate, glue, and scissors to each child so they can make their own face glyphs. This activity requires a great deal of guidance and discussion. Instruct children to start with the data *Girl or Boy*. Direct attention to the legend on the chart and review several of the symbols to reinforce what they represent. *What symbol represents a girl?* (Bow) *What symbol represents a boy?* (Bow) *If boys and girls have the same symbol on the glyph, how will we know which is which?* (From bow's location on the plate) Have children cut out the symbol, determine where it should be placed, and glue it onto the plate.

f.y.i.

You might want to streamline the different phases of creating the glyph. It is easier for children to color the parts of the bows before they cut the student page apart. They are also less likely to lose the parts of the face if all of the coloring is done in one step.

Repeat the procedure for *Family* representation. Have children select the symbol for the descriptions that apply to them, color it the appropriate color, cut it out, and paste it onto their plate. Instruct them to select, cut out, and paste a symbol for each data category. As children work, circulate and monitor their progress by asking children to explain their choice of symbols.

After each feature has been added to the paper plates, hold up a plate or two and ask children to interpret the information represented. *What can you tell about this person?* If the children have difficulties interpreting the data, ask one question at a time. *Does this person have a pet? What kind? Is this person an only child?*

Ask children to check their completed glyphs against the legend to be sure the correct information is shown. Then invite children to bring their glyphs to the front of the class and have a volunteer summarize the information displayed. Ask the volunteer to explain how he/she knows what the face represents. Ask the class if they agree or disagree with the summary and to explain why. Children should be able to validate each point by referring to the legend.

f.y.i.

You might want to use the floor to lay out the bar graphs. That way you and the children can graph the glyphs in many different ways. It is also easy to align the glyphs on the floor, making the number comparisons more apparent.

Now ask children to suggest different ways the completed glyphs might be sorted and record a few suggestions. Children might suggest sorting by the different information categories. Sort the glyphs according to one of the suggestions and have children make a bar graph by arranging their glyphs in columns. Focus on interpreting the information represented by the graph.

- *Do more children in our class walk to school or take the bus? How do you know?*
- *How can you tell if there are more children with sisters than brothers?*

- *What kinds of pets are the most common among the children in this class? How do you know?*
- *Are there more boys or girls in this class?*
- *Can you tell from the glyphs whether more children have dogs or cats?*

CONCLUDE THE LESSON spending as much time as possible sorting and re-sorting the glyphs. Each time, ask questions to focus the children on the data that the graph shows. Be sure to include questions that cannot be answered by the graph. *How many sisters and brothers are there in all? Why can you not tell this?*

Save the glyphs to make new bar graphs. You can use those graphs as models for children to make permanent bar graphs of individual pieces of information.

Student Pages

Student pages 126–127 contain the features children will use to make the glyphs.

Assessment

Children's completed glyphs, their answers to questions about the glyphs, and their summaries of glyphs allowed you to determine whether they understood that the features symbolize data. The sorting and graphing of the glyphs helped you to determine whether children were able to focus on specific attributes. You were also able to determine whether children could describe and compare data represented in graph form.

NCTM Standards Summary

Children represented information about themselves by using shapes and colors to create glyphs. They used a class-made legend as a key to represent information and to analyze the data of others. They shared their understanding about the data by interpreting and summarizing glyphs. They sorted their glyphs by properties and made bar graphs to represent specific sets of data. They then compared the data and quantified information in the graphs.

Answers

Pages 126–127
There are no answers for these pages.

Name

Representing Data

Color the symbols. Cut them out.
Paste them on the paper plate.

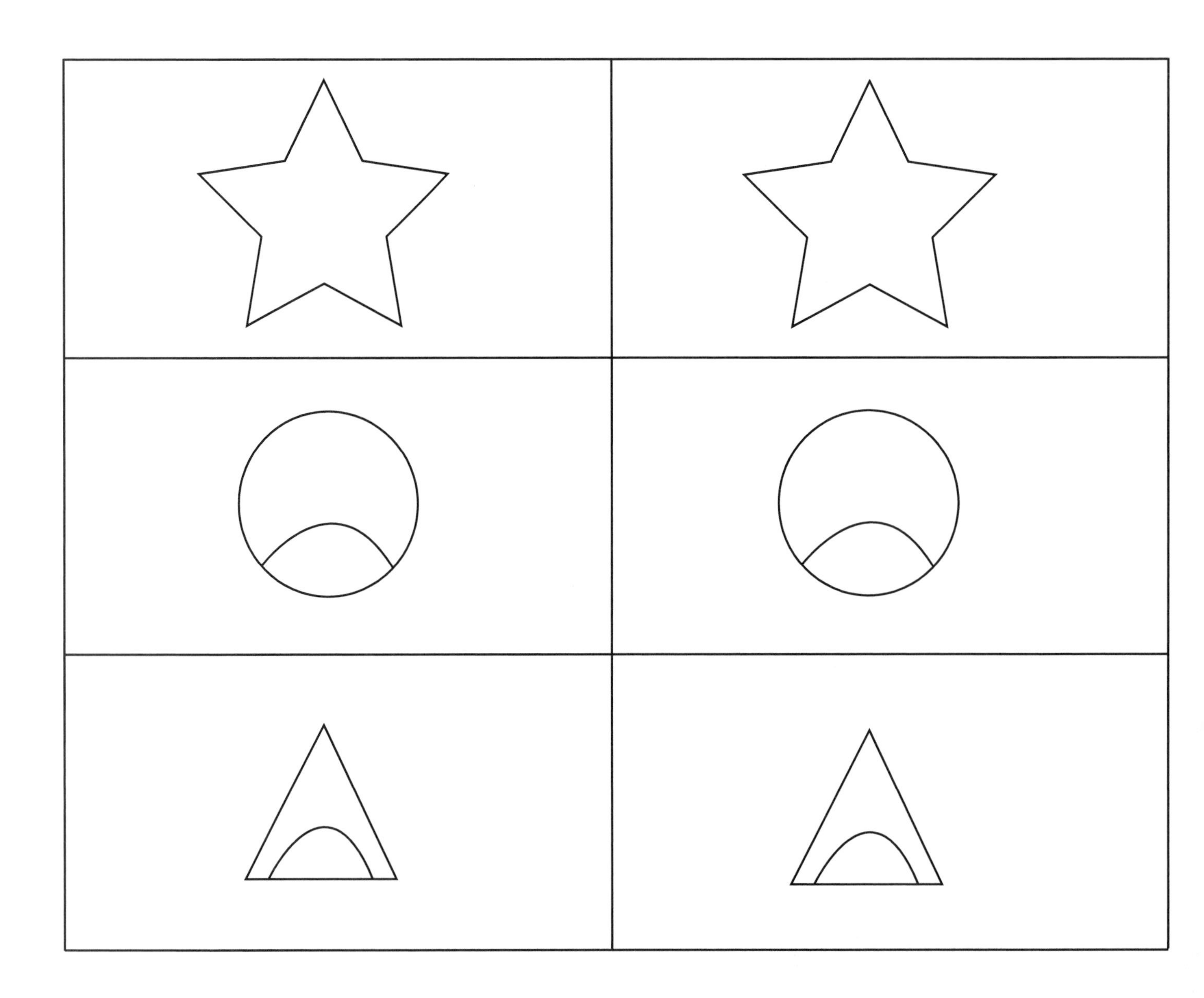

Name ______________________________

Representing Data

Color the symbols. Cut them out.
Paste them on the paper plate.

Predicting Outcomes

Introduction

Objective → Children will make predictions and verify them using a simple probability experiment.

Context → Children have made predictions, recorded information and checked their predictions. They will continue predicting, recording, and verifying information. This lesson is best done in the latter part of the school year.

NCTM Standards Focus

In this standards-based lesson, children explore different outcomes in an experiment. As children decide how to make their predictions based on the contents in a bag, they employ reasoning and proof. They talk about what is possible and impossible in their daily lives. This lesson provides opportunities to explore with concrete materials, which children should experience before being introduced to theoretical probability.

Reasoning and Proof Children make predictions about possible outcomes for selection based on a set of concrete materials. They use reasoning to explain why their predictions are possible or impossible.

Communication Children discuss possible outcomes for a probability experiment and explain why they believe an event will or will not occur.

Problem Solving Children use problem-solving strategies to solve the probability problems that are posed in the lesson.

Connections Children make connections between the items from which selections are being made, and the probability of an event occurring.

Teaching Plan

Materials → Student pages 132–133; 10 red counters and 10 yellow counters for whole class activity; 8 red counters and 2 yellow counters for each pair; 7 yellow and 3 red connecting cubes for each pair

OPEN THE LESSON by reviewing probability in a situation about the day's weather. Ask children questions like the following: *What is the weather like outside? Is it hot or cold? Is it raining or snowing? Do you think it will* (select the most improbable response) *snow today?*

After the children have responded that "it" is unlikely to occur, tell them that today the class will discuss probability. *Probability is the chance that something will—or will not—happen.* It is like saying something "probably will happen." *Will we probably have lunch today?* (Yes.) It's also like saying something "probably will not happen." *Will the sun probably go down by lunchtime?* (No.)

Explain to children that they are going to decide the probability of picking a certain color from a bag of counters. Display a paper bag and 10 red counters, and then place the counters into the bag. *What color counter do you think we will pick out of the bag?* (Red) *Are you sure that you will pick a red counter? How can you be sure?* Explain that when you are sure that something will happen, you can say that you are *certain*.

Continue questioning the children. *Is it probable that I can pick a yellow counter from this bag?* (No.) *How do you know?* (There aren't any yellow counters in the bag.) Explain that when they know that an event cannot occur, the event is said to be *impossible*.

Take the red counters out of the bag and replace them with 10 yellow counters. *How many counters are there? How many yellow counters are there? Are you certain that I will select a yellow counter? Explain why.*

NEXT, PLACE 8 RED COUNTERS and 2 yellow counters in a bag. Shake the bag. Invite a volunteer to pick a counter from the bag, but first ask the class what they think will happen. *Do you think a red counter or a yellow counter will be picked? Why?* Children should explain that since most of the counters (8) are red, a red counter would probably be picked. *Can you be certain that a red counter will be picked?* (No.) Children should explain that there are 2 yellow counters in the bag and one of them might be picked. *What makes you think so?* After one counter has been selected, discuss whether the same result would always occur or be more likely or less likely to occur again.

f.y.i.

The best strategy for making the correct prediction in this exercise is to always choose red since red has the best chance of being picked. If no child tried predicting red each time, ask children why someone might use that strategy.

What Might Happen . . . What to Do

Some children might think that the red and yellow colors should form a pattern or take turns coming out of the bag. For example, if a red cube has been picked for 3 times in a row they may think it is yellow's turn. In a lighthearted way, while you are discussing what is happening, you might ask the students how the counters would know whose turn it is—do they talk to each other? Children need to begin to see that each event or draw of the cube is independent of any other event or draw.

f.y.i.

Having children show thumbs up or down enables you to get a quick read of their thinking and to assess the general understanding of the class as a whole. To discourage children who are unsure from waiting to see what others do, you might want to encourage children to keep their signaling thumbs close to their chests.

Next, distribute student page 132 and tell children that the class will do an experiment. Tell them you are going to put 7 red cubes and 3 yellow cubes into a bag. You will pick out one cube at a time from the bag and put it back into the bag. Explain that before a counter is picked, you want them to *predict* (say what will happen) whether the cube will be red or yellow. You want them to indicate their prediction with a thumbs-up or a thumbs-down vote—thumbs up for red and thumbs down for yellow. Then, they are to record their prediction in the appropriate column on student page 132. Make sure children understand that after each cube is picked it will be returned to the bag; each time you pick from the bag there will be 7 red cubes and 3 yellow cubes.

On the board, draw a table like the one on student page 132 to record results, but do not record anything in the *Prediction* column. Then, pick a cube from the bag and record the result in the column labeled *Actual*. Instruct children to record the result on their papers. Have children compare the actual result with their predictions and discuss why they made the predictions they did. Hearing the thinking of others will help expand children's thinking as they consider future predictions.

Continue to pick and replace cubes until you have picked ten times. Before each pick, ask the children to predict, give a thumb vote (up for red, down for yellow), and record their predictions. Then, draw a cube from the bag, record the result, and have children record it on their papers. Have children compare their predictions to the result and briefly discuss. Encourage them to discuss the overall outcome of the experiment. *Do you think the results of the experiment make sense? Did you change how you made your predictions as we did the experiment? Explain.*

If time permits try this activity with a different mix of counters. Then ask the children how they could set up the experiment so that they could always predict correctly.

Student Pages

Student page 132 contains a table for children to record information about the class experiment. Student page 133 has simulated results from experiments and questions for children to answer.

Assessment

You had opportunities to assess children's ability to predict possible outcomes and to determine their comfort level with the use of ideas such as *more likely*, or *less likely* using everyday language such as *possible* or *impossible.* You could judge children's thinking as they responded to the many *whys* posed in this lesson.

NCTM Standards Summary

Throughout the lesson, children used reasoning as they made predictions about what color counter was most likely to be picked out of a bag. They made connections between the colors available to select from and possible outcomes. They communicated thinking verbally, with thumb votes, and in written form, and they explained how they made their predictions. As children discussed factors that influenced their predictions, they had an opportunity to affirm their thinking and listen to ways of thinking that might not have occurred to them.

Answers

Page 132
Answers may vary.

Page 133
1. Shaded
2. Shaded
3. White
4. Shaded
5. White

Name ____________________

Predicting Outcomes

Use this as your recording sheet.
Complete the chart.
Write red or yellow.

Pick	Prediction	Actual
1		
2		
3		
4		
5		
6		
7		
8		
9		
10		

Name

Predicting Outcomes

Ring the color most likely to be picked.

1.

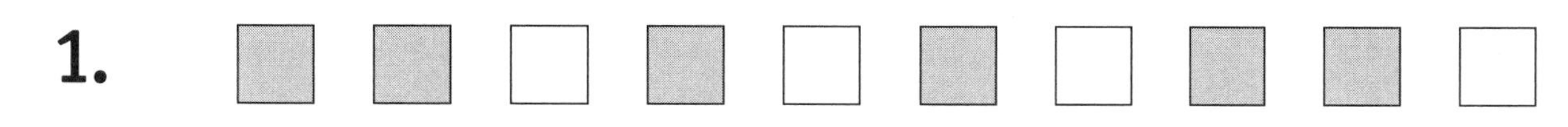

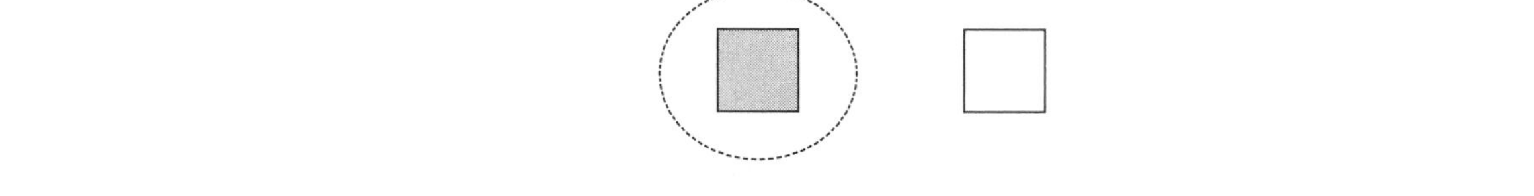

2.

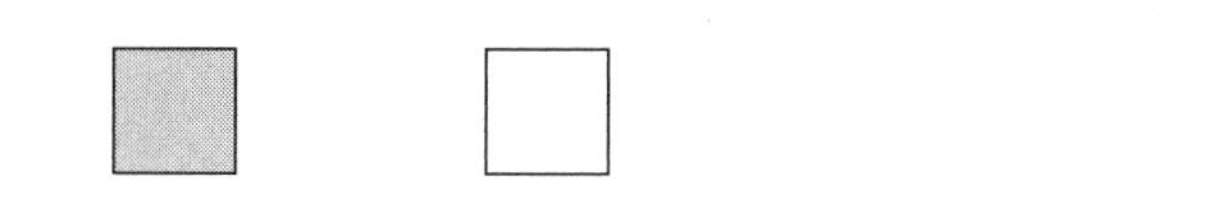

3.

4.

5.

Recognizing the Mode of a Data Set

Introduction

Objective → The children will determine the range and mode of a set of data then represent it in a graph.

Context → Children have represented data using bar graphs. They have compared and described the data in line plots. They will continue generating, recording, and representing data using probability experiments.

NCTM Standards Focus

Children are often given data symbolically and told how to interpret it. This does not require the same type of involvement as when they generate and then represent the data themselves. In this standards-based lesson, children generate the data and show it in a physical graph before changing the data to a line plot.

Representation Children use connecting links to generate data. They represent the data using physical graphs and a line plot.

Communication Children interpret data and describe the mode and the range of the data set.

Connections Children connect the data they generate with the new concepts of range and mode. They also connect the data to graphical representations.

Teaching Plan

Materials → Student pages 138–139; 40 connecting links for each child; chart paper

TELL CHILDREN THAT THEY ARE GOING TO put together connecting links for exactly one minute. You may wish to let them practice for a bit so they feel they are prepared. Tell them that once they have this information, or data, they will display it so people can see it and understand it quickly. Have children work for a minute and then have them record how many they put together.

When children are finished, arrange the data so children can see all the results. You can create both a human graph and record the information on the board at the same time. To create the graph, first find the child who connected the fewest links.

Ask the child with the fewest links to stand at a given spot in the room. (Since you will be creating a human graph, make sure they stand to the far left side of what will be your graph.) Make sure all other children who had the same number of links stand one behind the other. Continue in this manner until all the children are standing up.

At the same time, create a simple pictograph, using an X to represent each child, and to show how many children connected a certain number of links. This type of graph will be easy to turn into a line plot later on.

Ask children what was the fewest number of links that were connected and what was the most. Show both numbers on a number line. Now have children find the distance between the two numbers. Tell them that this is the range of the data. The *range* tells over how many possible values the data is spread.

NEXT, ASK THEM TO FIND OUT what number of links was most often connected by the children. Tell children that we call this data value the *mode* of the data. For example, the mode in the line plot below is 32. Children may be able to remember mode and what it means because it sounds somewhat like "most."

Now tell children that you are going to show them a new way to show this type of information; a line plot. Draw the outline of a line plot for the data children generated by connecting links.

A line plot uses both horizontal and vertical lines to help show the data. By using the range, you can select the two end points of the graph. You may wish to have the points a little farther out than the two end points. In the example below, the line plot has vertical lines for even numbers and the spaces in between them represent the odd numbers. The horizontal lines help represent the number in each segment.

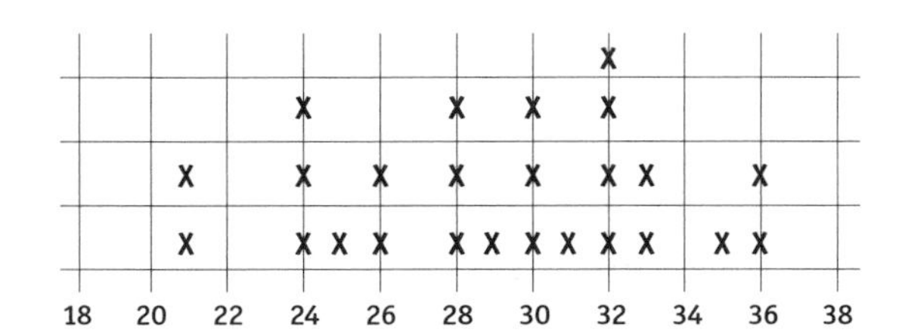

f.y.i.

Connecting links are good for this activity. They are easy to handle and fun for the children to use. If links are not available, the activity can be done with anything that can be done for one minute and that can easily be timed. For example, children can draw circles, write the alphabet, or write numbers 1 through 9 over and over. Keep the activity fun and light; try to make sure children don't see it as a contest but as a way to generate data.

Make the line plot on the board and ask the children to use the information from the board to help. Ask them where to start the graph and how much room they think they need to leave in the middle of the graph. Show them the number system and have them tell which numbers should go under the lines. Once the line plot is finished, ask children to explain how it shows the information. Ask them questions about the data that can be answered by looking at the line plot and ask them to think up questions to ask other children. Also review the concepts of range and mode using the line plot.

f.y.i.

You might want to have the children create a line plot on the board as they line up rather than doing it yourself. Draw the outline of the line plot on the board. List the values of the numbers of links the children made from smallest to largest. As each child goes to get in line, he or she should make an X where his or her value would appear on the plot. Be sure that every child can see the line plot as it is being created.

What Might Happen . . . What to Do

Some children might have trouble understanding the concept of mode or recognizing how to find this information using the line plot. Have these children look for the tallest line on the plot.

To end the lesson, review student pages 138 and 139. Have children complete the pages either with a partner or individually.

Student Pages

Student page 138 provides a line plot that shows the number of letters in the first names of children. Student page 139 contains another line plot that shows the number of hours children played outside on a Saturday.

Assessment

You observed and listened to the children as they responded to questions about how to represent data and what the data tells them. The children's answers on the student pages gave you additional information about whether they understood how to use line plots and what specific information they got from them.

NCTM Standards Summary

The children generated, represented, and interpreted the data physically and then showed the same data on a line plot. They looked at the distribution of the data and isolated the mode and the range of the data set. They interpreted the representations of Xs above the horizontal axis as the number of children who had connected that many links. Children communicated their understanding of the physical and symbolic representations to the class.

Answers

Page 138

1. 9 letters
2. 4 letters
3. The range is 5.
4. The mode is 4.
5. The column for 4 is the tallest.

Page 139

1. 1 hour
2. 8 hours
3. The range is 7.
4. 6
5. That column is the tallest.

Name ________________________

Recognizing the Mode of a Data Set

The line plot shows the number of letters in the first names of children in a class. Use the line plot to answer the questions.

Number of Letters in the First Names of Our Classmates

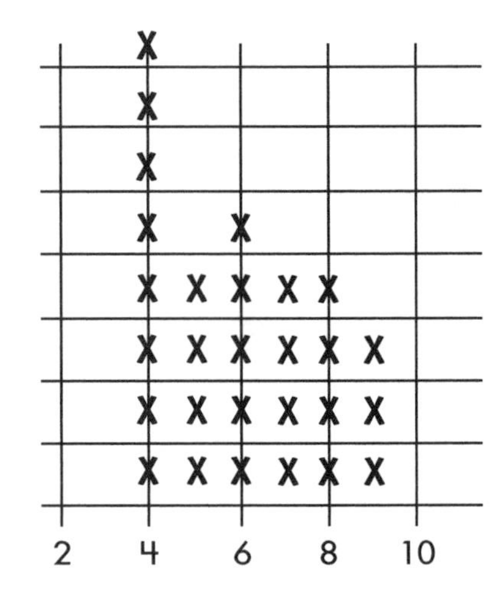

1. What is the fewest number of letters in the first names?

____

2. What is the greatest number of letters in the first names?

____

3. What is the range?

____

4. What is the mode?

____

5. How do you know?

____

Name

Recognizing the Mode of a Data Set

The line plot shows how many hours children played outside on Saturday. Use the line plot to answer the questions.

Number of Hours We Played Outside on Saturday

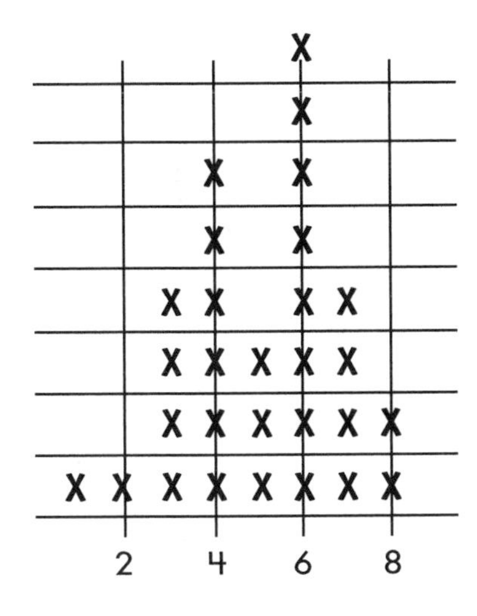

1. What is the fewest number of hours the children played outside on Saturday?

2. What is the greatest number of hours the children played outside on Saturday?

3. What is the range?

4. What is the mode?

5. How do you know?

Interpreting Bar Graphs

Introduction

Objective → Children will interpret a bar graph.

Context → Children have compared, added, and subtracted numbers up to 12. In later lessons, they will use collected data to make their own bar graphs.

Name ______________________

Interpreting Bar Graphs

Learn

Maya saw different kinds of butterflies in the park.

Butterflies Maya Saw

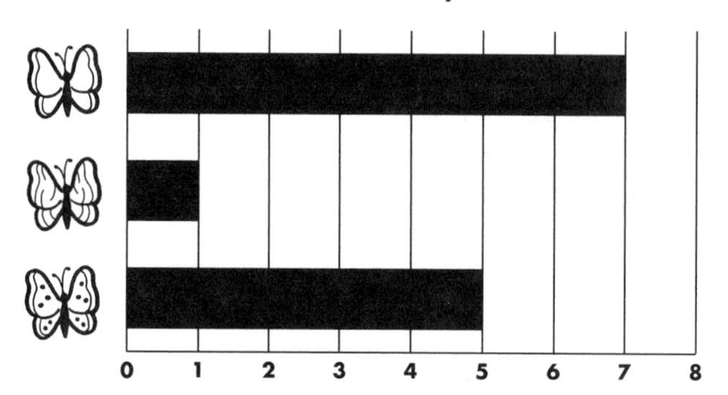

1. How many did she see? ________
2. Did she see more or more ? ________
3. Ring the butterfly she saw the most.   
4. Ring the butterfly she saw the least.  

NCTM Process Standards Analysis and Focus

The standards analysis examines how the process standards have been incorporated into the above lesson. By increasing the focus on three of the process standards, a more effective and meaningful lesson can be presented. The suggestions offered can help you to think about how this might be accomplished.

Communication Children identify familiar objects as they read bar graphs and answer questions. The teachers' notes suggest that children share information they know about the various objects.

Suggestion → **Discuss what a graph is and the purpose graphs serve. Also discuss the different parts of a graph and the specific information that can be gleaned from each part. This will give**

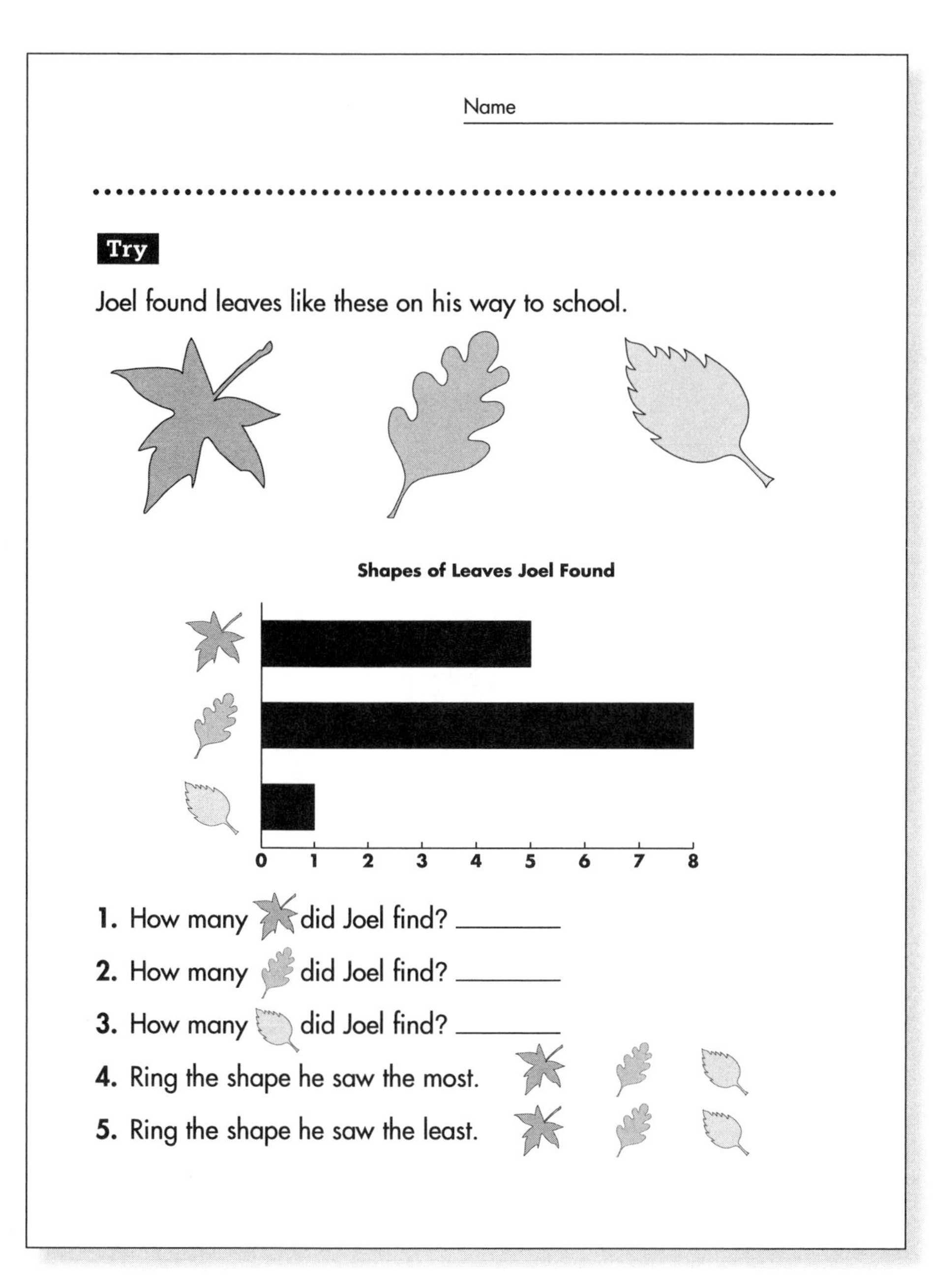

Name ________________

Try

Joel found leaves like these on his way to school.

Shapes of Leaves Joel Found

1. How many [leaf] did Joel find? ______
2. How many [leaf] did Joel find? ______
3. How many [leaf] did Joel find? ______
4. Ring the shape he saw the most.
5. Ring the shape he saw the least.

children a better understanding of the types of questions that can be answered by graphs and what to look for when reading a graph.

Representation Horizontal bar graphs are presented with symbols representing the objects being graphed. Numerals along the horizontal axis represent numbers of objects.

***Suggestion* → Present collected data in both horizontal and vertical orientations. Use words as well as pictures to represent objects or topics being graphed. Include counting by twos and other counting intervals to represent numbers of objects. Presenting the collected data in more than one way will strengthen children's ability to interpret graphs.**

Reasoning and Proof Children are asked questions that require them to refer back to a given graph to locate specific information. However, the questions do not encourage interpretation of the information.

***Suggestion* → Encourage children to make comparisons, interpretations, and predictions based on the information presented in the graphs. Allow time for children to explain their thinking and how they determined their answers. Have children use specific information from the graphs to support their interpretations.**

Connections The bar graphs incorporate familiar objects that children can find in their immediate environment.

Problem Solving While this lesson focuses on examining bar graphs and answering questions about them, problem solving is not involved.

The teaching plan that follows shows how the suggestions for increasing the focus on the process standards can be implemented.

Revised Teaching Plan

f.y.i.

It is best to limit the number of items included in each graph to fewer than five. For example, if you graph favorite ice cream flavors, you might include these five categories: vanilla, strawberry, chocolate, chocolate chip, and other (this last category would be used for all other flavors).

Materials → Chart paper; markers; transparencies; overhead projector

PRIOR TO THE LESSON, gather information from the class about familiar topics such as favorite ice cream flavors, pets, number of siblings, and so on. Personalizing the information presented not only makes it more interesting for children, but also allows them to get a better understanding of the types of questions that can be answered from given data. Then use the information from one of the topics to construct simple bar graphs and a table on a transparency or chart paper. Present the information in three ways, as follows:

- as a graph showing data with horizontal bars and numbers in intervals of one
- as a graph with vertical bars and numbers in intervals of two
- as a table showing the same information that is in the graphs

Be sure to title each graph as well as the table.

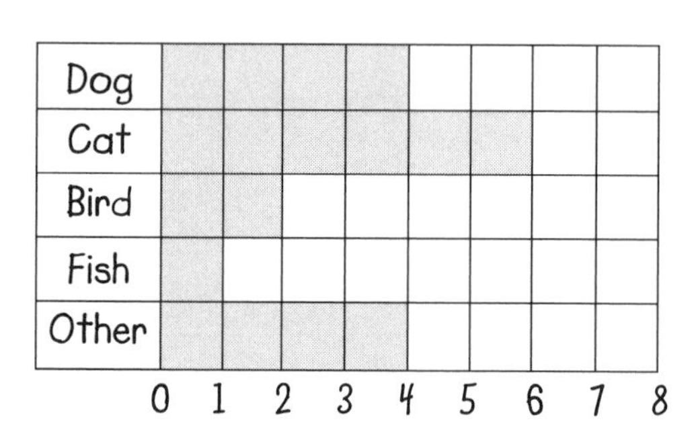

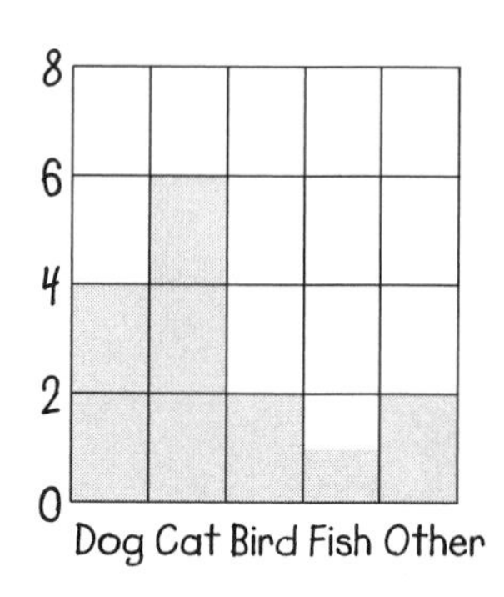

FOCUS ATTENTION ON ONE of the bar graphs that you have prepared in advance. Explain that the graph is useful in organizing information. *Why do you think that this graph is called a bar graph?* Help children to briefly identify general information about the graph. *How do we know what this graph is about?* (The title gives us this information.) Draw children's attention to the different categories represented on the graph. *How do we know which animals are represented?* (Types of animals are listed along the vertical axis.) *How does the graph show the number of each pet represented?* (Numbers appear along the horizontal axis.) Demonstrate how to use the information along each axis as you read the graph. Ask specific questions that can be answered by looking at the graph. *Are there fewer pet birds then pet fish? How many different pets are shown?* Questions of this sort help children to refine the types of questions they are able to ask to obtain information from graphs.

Pose questions to further investigate the types of information that can be gleaned from the graph. *Can you tell from this graph if there are more cats or more dogs? How can you tell? Can you tell if there are more birds or more fish? Can you tell which animal there are the fewest of? The most? Can you tell how many children in the class have pets?* (Children should understand that if there are 5 dogs shown, that doesn't necessarily mean that five children each have a dog. Perhaps one child has 2 dogs.) *Who has a dog? A cat?* (That information is not available.) *Does anyone have a pet rabbit?* (It is possible that a rabbit is among the animals in the group "other," but we don't know for sure.) Allow time for children to explain their observations. Through discussion, children have an opportunity to clarify their thinking.

f.y.i.

Help children to become aware of the variety of bar graphs. Provide children with newspapers and magazines, asking them to find and cut out bar graphs. Display these on a bulletin board. Ask questions about the displayed graphs to help children think about the information represented. Opportunities for children to note ways in which graphs are used in the real world will help them to see the relevance of this mathematical concept.

CALL ATTENTION TO THE TABLE that you have prepared in advance. Ask children to compare it to the graph. If necessary, point out how the table gives the same information as the graph. Challenge children to consider why someone would want to make a graph when the information can be put in a table format. Explain that a graph makes the information easy to compare. *If two more children joined our class today, how might the information in our table change? How would that affect the graph?* Take time to discuss how additional children with pets might change the information in both the table and the graph. If time permits, illustrate changes on the graph.

Our Pets		Total
Dog	////	4
Cat	~~////~~ /	6
Bird	//	2
Fish	/	1
Other	////	4

Next, point to the second graph on the transparency or chart paper. Point out or ask children to note the differences between the two graphs: bars are horizontal on this graph, numbers are in intervals of two. Have volunteers count by 2s as they glean information from the graph. Ask questions similar to those asked for the first graph. Be sure to include questions that ask if there are more than and how many more. Draw attention to bars that fill only half the interval and ask children how they would interpret that information. Experiences such as these deepen understanding of viewing and interpreting graphical information.

CONCLUDE THE LESSON by asking children to summarize what they have learned about bar graphs. Record the information on a chart and have it available in the math center. The summary chart should have information similar to the following:

- Bar graphs show information.
- You can look at a bar graph and quickly tell someone about the information.
- They make it easier to compare things.
- Sometimes the bars go up and sometimes they go across.
- A graph needs a title to tell what it is about.

Student Pages

Children should now be ready to complete exercises similar to those on the reduced student pages.

Assessment

As children read and interpreted information from the two graphs during whole-class discussions, there were opportunities to determine their level of understanding. Allowing time for children to explain their completed student pages provides another means by which to assess children's comprehension.

NCTM Standards Summary

Activities that promote listening and speaking helped children to make sense of the mathematical concepts presented in the lesson. These experiences encouraged children to formulate ideas about ways to process information as they worked with graphs and shared ideas. Probing questions helped children to focus on the types of information that can be interpreted from graphs. Different representations of the collected data demonstrated how to organize information. Using both words and pictures helped children to see alternative ways to present information. Children refined their thoughts and understandings as they used their own words to interpret the information from the graphs. Experiences such as these helped to increase children's confidence and competence.

Create Your Own Lesson

THIS LAST CHAPTER IS DESIGNED TO HELP you develop your own lessons in which you can comfortably incorporate the NCTM standards with your teaching style. We start with a list of questions to help you focus on factors to consider as you begin to organize a standards-based lesson. Then, we model the process used to create a lesson as you are walked through the thoughts and decisions one person used in developing a lesson.

The questions listed here are meant as a guide, a starting point; they are offered to get you thinking about how to develop your lesson, what material to cover, what steps to follow, what questions to ask. Hopefully, these questions will trigger additional ideas that you will add as you go along.

Write down the ideas that come to you as you read each question. There may be questions for which you don't have an immediate response, but don't worry; as you begin working on your lesson, ideas will come. Start by selecting the general content area. Think about the concept you want to develop. Then, narrow in on an objective for the lesson. Be specific—and be realistic. What does meeting that objective mean? Is there a skill that children should be able to perform after completing the lesson? Are there questions they should be able to answer? How will you determine that the objective has been met?

Next, think about the process standards: Problem Solving, Reasoning and Proof, Communication, Connections, and Representation. What approach will be effective in helping children understand the concept? Try to envision how the lesson will flow, how it should begin, what activities and questions will be included, and how you will assess learning. Understand that there can be several ways to successfully teach any lesson. As you begin to design your lesson, new ideas will come and you will be able to refine your thinking.

Focusing Questions

1. What content standard is to be addressed? What concept within that standard is to be developed?

2. What information do the standards offer about this content?

3. What do children know about this content? What don't they know?

4. What is the specific objective of the lesson? What should children be able to do at the end of the lesson?

recognize	**identify**	**define**
review	**compute**	**classify**
compare	**create**	**other**

5. What kinds of questions should children be able to answer when they complete this lesson? What skill(s) should they be able to demonstrate?

6. What resources are available to develop this concept?

references	**textual material**
manipulatives	**supplementary material**
colleagues	**student knowledge**

7. What can realistically be accomplished in the time allowed?

8. Which activities and process standards can best help develop the key ideas?
   - exploring using manipulatives (Representation)
   - using drawings, charts, diagrams (Representation)
   - focusing on symbols (Representation)
   - conducting small-group/large-group discussion (Communication)
   - having children gather and analyze data (Problem Solving)
   - thinking through relationships and explaining them (Reasoning and Proof and Communication)
   - finding ways to prove thinking and verify solutions (Reasoning and Proof)
   - extending/building on former knowledge (Connections)
   - integrating the concept with another discipline (Connections)
   - relating math to its use in the real world (Connections)

9. What questions will focus thinking on the concept and help guide learning?

Developing the Lesson

I WOULD LIKE TO DEVELOP A LESSON that focuses on patterns, part of Content Standard 2: Algebra. However, I'd like to go further than simply having the children imitate patterns. Previously, when I have planned for my class to work with patterns, I have followed textbooks and had my children imitate patterns using manipulatives. I have generally used attribute blocks to do this. Repeating the pattern was an end in itself. I never got the feeling that the children understood the concept of patterns in a broader mathematical sense. I'd like to present my children with an active experience that will allow them to develop a definition of patterns as we proceed with the lesson.

Most of my children will be able to look at a simple pattern made out of manipulatives and replicate it using the same manipulatives—or they will be able to with a little bit of practice. Most of them can extend simple patterns, but as they see patterns that are more complex, they seem to get confused. I am not sure they can pick the initial pattern segment out of an extension of the pattern. Can they develop an accurate definition of a pattern of their own? I'd like them to look at patterns in a more general way and be able to relate the patterns to each other. I want to introduce them to the fact that a "red, yellow, red, yellow" pattern is similar to a "green, blue, green, blue, green blue" pattern.

While recognizing similarities in patterns will help them in the study of patterns, how can I can this connect to their lives? Creating a definition of patterns could provide a way for my children to organize the world around them. For instance, they might notice that conifer trees have flat, skinny leaves, and most other trees have broad, flat leaves.

I wonder if my children realize how many patterns there are in their daily life. They can probably recognize patterns in their clothes, or in tiles in the bathroom, or maybe even patterns in rhymes they like to say. But do they see that our school week is a pattern—that Tuesday and Thursday we go to Science Lab? I'm really getting carried way, but I'd be curious to see if, after the lesson, the children will be able to translate recognizing a pattern in something concrete like manipulatives to other things present in their lives.

My objectives for the lesson are for the children to first analyze a pattern, then identify the segment that repeats, then extend the pattern, and then begin to generalize what a pattern is.

Process skills will be inherent in these activities. The children will be using reasoning as I ask them to look at, and think about, what makes something a pattern. They will be using representation as they make and extend patterns with manipulatives and drawings. Communication will be important as they discuss their ideas with each other, describe how they extend the pattern, and attempt to come up with their own definition of a pattern.

My first goal will be to introduce the concept of patterns in our own environment. I will want all of the children to get the same information. To accomplish this, I will need to work with the whole group. That way, I can introduce patterns by pointing them out to the children, and also have the children point out patterns in the room. Once that has happened, we can look for the initial pattern segment and gain a better understanding of what makes something a pattern. I want the children to get hands-on work at this stage of the lesson, but this is new and crucial information, so I want to continue with the whole-class lesson. If all goes well, we will try to break a pattern down into its simplest form. While we will not be identifying a pattern as an *ABAB* pattern, we will be trying to make a different representations of the same pattern.

As I look around the classroom, I can see there are several patterns in the room that I can use. For instance, the checked border around the bulletin board; the repeating splashes of red, yellow, and blue brush strokes that are printed on the art smocks; and the green, gray, and yellow tiles that are interspersed in the tiles of the floor. Those things will provide a good beginning to for a discussion on patterns that we can find around us.

Besides the patterns found in the classroom, I will need to make sure I have enough of some manipulative to use for the first part of the lesson. When we move on to the second part of the lesson, I will have to provide a variety of writing and drawing materials.

I have some simple activities in mind that will hopefully lead to some good discussion. I don't think our initial exploration of patterns will take very long.

I'll start by having the children look at and try to find patterns in the room, then I'll pose a problem-solving question that will get the children thinking about patterns. First, we'll look at and analyze the border on the bulletin board. After the children describe what they see, I want to introduce the word *pattern*. I would like them to try to define what pattern means. After we agree on a definition, I'll encourage the children to use the definition to describe what they see in other pattern situations.

I could say, *Tell me about the border.* I am sure they will quickly note that it has alternating black squares and white squares. Then I will ask, *When we say that the border of the bulletin board border is black square, white square, black square, white square, is there a word to describe what the squares are making?* Hopefully, some of the children will say the squares are making a pattern. If they don't, I'll tell them that the word that describes what the squares are making is *pattern*. I'll ask *Can you tell me what a pattern is?* I think they might say things like "It's the same over and over," or "Black squares and white squares keep going." I want to make sure that they at least talk about the repeating. When that happens I will ask them what is it that is repeating. I want to ask that question because it will set up the one of the most important parts of the lesson, which is to find out the initial segment or what repeats. I feel this is important because when they extend a pattern, what they are really doing is repeating that initial segment. I want to make sure they understand that rather than guessing how to make a pattern repeat. They will need a more sophisticated level of understanding when they start looking at more complex patterns.

Next, I will call the children's attention to a similar patern such as the pattern on their art smocks, and ask them if they see a pattern. I will say, *Tell me about the pattern you see in the art smocks.* I'll ask, *If there is a pattern on the art smocks, and a pattern on the bulletin board, why aren't the patterns the same?* This is a very important question because it gets children to think about individual patterns and the differences between patterns. Their answers will help me to know if they are able to begin to generalize a pattern as something that repeats and can be represented in different ways. Later in the lesson, we will reverse this thinking as we begin to see how patterns that may look different can be seen as the same.

The children should now be ready to point out other patterns they see in the room. I might start by directing their attention to the tiles.

Now that they are able to recognize patterns, we are going to look for and identify the initial segment of a pattern. As I stated earlier, this is what children need to do before they extend the pattern, however we usually just ask them to extend the pattern and don't focus on the skill necessary for extending the pattern. I'll pull out the manipulatives, probably rainbow tiles or another manipulative where each one is the same size and shape, but a different color, so only one attribute is different. Since we are working on something they haven't focused on before, I don't want anything acting as a distracter. I'll make a pattern, repeating the pattern twice. It is essential that I always repeat the pattern at least twice so the children can see it repeat, otherwise I haven't really established a pattern. I'll ask the children to imitate at their desks what they see.

I'll ask the children, *What can you tell me about this pattern?* After a few children have explained the pattern, red green, yellow, red, green, yellow, I'll ask the children to show it to me. I'll circulate as children are making their patterns. Because my objective is to have the children identify a segment of a pattern, I'll ask, *You've told me that a pattern is the same 'over and over', but can you find the part that keeps repeating over and over?* When a child believes he or she has identified the segment, I will ask him or her to represent it verbally. *What is the part that gets repeated over and over?* I will repeat this process of showing different patterns, asking the children to determine if it is a pattern, then analyze it for the segment and then extend it. I want the children to get used to the order of first making sure a pattern exists, then finding the initial segment, and then extending the pattern. While I know many of them do this informally, I want them to think about it. As soon as many of the children are able to do this, I will introduce the word "segment". *You can call the part that repeats a segment. What's the segment in this pattern?* If only a few children use the word segment as they describe one, that's OK. It is not a formal term but it best describes what they are looking for. I want to make sure the others are at least able to describe a segment in a particular pattern. I'll ask them to work in pairs for a few minutes taking turns making patterns for each other to imitate and identify the segment.

If I am feeling confident that my class is getting the idea of patterns, then I'll be ready to show them another kind of pattern—a different manifestation as the standard says. I'll suddenly stomp my foot twice, then clap, then repeat the stomping and clapping. I'll ask them to join in. I have purposely picked a pattern that is not visual, but rather, one that uses sound. That way when I ask children to draw the pattern, they will have to represent it in a way that is different from what they hear because they can't draw a sound. This will give us a situation that will allow the children to see the same pattern represented differently.

After the children have imitated my stomp, stomp, clap several times, and they have quieted down, I'll ask them *Was the sound you were making a pattern? Why?* I have no idea how they will respond. Hopefully they will say it is a pattern, because like the manipulatives in the previous activity, or the border on the bulletin board, it has a segment that repeats. If they don't, I can prompt them to see it is a pattern by reminding them about the patterns in the rainbow tiles. *Why did the rainbow tiles make patterns?* I'll lead them to remember the patterns had a repeated segment. Then I'll stomp, stomp, clap several times. *What's the segment in what you hear?*

Next, because I want them to begin to see that a pattern is a repeated segment that can be represented in different ways, I'll distribute drawing materials and invite them to show me the stomp, stomp, clap. I imagine they might use feet and hands to represent the noise. I will be curious to see if they represent the pattern in a linear fashion, the way we have used the rainbow tiles, or as more of a free-form expression. I'll tell them that if they need help remembering the pattern, just stomp, stomp, clap again. When all the children have completed the task, I will ask *What are some ways you made the stomp, stomp, clap pattern?* After they have shared some of their representations, I'll ask them how the patterns are different from one another and how they are similar. It is important for them to see that while the patterns may look different, they are drawings of the same pattern. Now they can begin to see how different patterns can be related because they may have the same structure. I know this will be difficult for some children to see, so I will have to see how far I can take this.

If things are going well, I will either put up on the board or make three p atterns. I will make a red, blue, red, blue pattern with the shapes, a yellow, yellow, green, yellow, yellow, green pattern, and a blue, yellow, blue, yellow pattern and ask them which two are similar and why. This should help me see if they are getting the idea that the red, blue and the blue, yellow are the ABAB type pattern and the yellow, yellow, green is a different type pattern.

Reviewing the Plan

I feel this lesson vastly improves upon how I taught patterns before. First, because I learned how patterns are significant in a larger, mathematical context I tried to incorporate that into the lesson. Also, I have tried to incorporate the process skills. I believe the learning in these activities is much more meaningful. The way I have planned this lesson requires them to reason, and communicate about patterns as well as make their own representations of patterns. These activities require more of the children than just asking them to extend a pattern on a page. I think they are really focusing on understanding mathematics and because of that, they can perform better on mathematical tasks.

DESIGN AND MAKE

BEDROOM FURNISHINGS

HEATHER LUKE

For Lisa

First published in 1996 by
New Holland Publishers (UK) Ltd
24 Nutford Place, London W1H
London • Cape Town • Sydney • Singapore

Reprinted in 1998

ISBN 1 85368 532 1 (hbk)
ISBN 1 85368 533 X (pbk)

Managing Editor: Gillian Haslam
Editor: Coral Walker
Designer: Kit Johnson
Photographer: David Johnson
Illustrations: Lizzie Sanders and Claire Davies

Typeset by Ace Filmsetters, Frome, Somerset
Reproduction byHirt and Carter (Pty) Ltd
Printed and bound in Malaysia by Times Offset (m) sdn Bhd

2 4 6 8 10 9 7 5 3

ACKNOWLEDGEMENTS

Thanks to my team, Sarah Westcott, Julie Troop and Jackie Pullman, for making the lovely soft furnishings shown throughout the book. To David Johnson for such stunning photographs and for working some miracles with the available light. To Yvonne, Gillian and Coral and Kit for the infinite time and patience needed to make words and pictures into a book. My gratitude to Gilda and Paul Chadd, Jano and Johnnie Clarke, Heather and Nicholas Phelps Brown, Andrew and Annie Stewart, George Stewart, Blair and Mary Stewart Wilson for the double priviledge of helping to decorate their lovely homes and then allowing me to photograph the results. And last, but not least, thanks to my husband Don and my children Peter, Michael and Lisa for their valuable contributions in all sorts of ways behind the scenes.

I would also like to thank the following suppliers for their help: Calluna for the fabrics on pages 21, 23, 31 and 37; Osbourne and Little for the fabrics on pages 24, 39 and 71 (bottom); Pierre Frey for the cushions on pages 29 and 46; Percheron for the toile de juoy on pages 43, 49, 67 and 77; Les Olivades for the fabrics on page 57; The Cartonnage Co. for the boxes on page 59; Chelsea Textiles for the fabrics on page 60; The White House for pillows and bedcovers on pages 19, 37, 38, 59, 67 and 73.
Photos on pages 21 and 70 by Tom Leighton/Homes and Gardens/Robert Harding Syndication

For soft furnishings course details contact Calluna Workshops, Hill House, Creech St Michael, Taunton, Somerset TA3 5DP. Fax: 01823 443335